Praise for Clear, Correct, Concise E-Mail

"Companies go to great lengths to hire and train people to represent them on the phone. Now that more and more customers are contacting businesses via e-mail, it's time to upgrade service representatives' skills with this clear and concise workbook. Short and to the point, this exercise-filled volume gets right to the heart of intelligent, professional online communication. Two thumbs up."

Jim Sterne, *Author, Customer Service on the Internet*

"A just-in-time training solution! If you're a customer service professional making the transition from phone to e-mail, this book will help you brush up on your writing skills. If you're a manager trying to hire or retain agents, this book will help you assess their writing skills and give them the training they need. If you're moving your customer service function online, you need a copy of this workbook for all your front-line agents who write e-mail."

Ron Muns, *CEO, Help Desk Institute*

"Finally, a much-needed book on properly handling e-mails from customers. E-mail is a very important customer service channel—our benchmark studies show e-mail comprises 25% of all contacts between customers and companies—and yet most companies totally underestimate the value of e-mail. I strongly recommend the *Clear, Correct, Concise E-Mail* workbook to all professionals responsible for corporate e-mail communications."

Dr. Jon Anton, *Director of Customer Service Benchmarking, Center for Customer-Driven Quality, Purdue University*

"Given the tremendous changes in customer support, many support professionals need to build new skill sets to keep pace with new technologies and customer's expectations. Because businesses now support customers over multiple channels (telephone, web, and e-mail), the ability to provide quality communication in writing becomes a competitive differentiator. Well-written customer support e-mail enhances the value and image of the company, the support organization, and the customer support professional.

The *Clear, Correct, Concise E-Mail* workbook is way overdue, and I applaud authors Marilynne Rudick and Leslie O'Flahavan for seeing the need and delivering a training tool that can benefit everyone on the front line."

Pete McGarahan, *Chairman, Help Desk 2000*

"The authors of **Clear, Correct, Concise E-Mail** know their stuff. Realistic examples, scenarios and practice items provide all the tools necessary to have your agents become e-mail customer service experts in no time. I highly recommend this workbook."

Ken Webb, *President, Sage Results*

"This amazing book is a must-have for every e-mail contact center. **Clear, Correct, Concise E-Mail** is both a bite-sized training workbook and a comprehensive reference manual. I started reading it and ended up completing the entire book in one sitting!

This workbook goes beyond the fundamentals of writing by incorporating universal customer service basics and covering trickier areas, such as how to avoid idioms and how to adjust the message for international customers.

The authors have created a workbook that can take agents with basic writing skills and turn them into polished professionals who consistently represent the company with a friendly, personalized approach."

Anita Rockwell, *Principal, The Rockwell Group, LLC*

Clear, Correct, Concise E-Mail:

A Writing Workbook for Customer Service Agents

By Marilynne Rudick and Leslie O'Flahavan

Clear, Correct, Concise E-Mail
A Writing Workbook for Customer Service Agents

by Marilynne Rudick and Leslie O'Flahavan

Published by:

E-WRITE
407 Scott Drive
Silver Spring, MD 20904 U.S.A.

Orders@WritingWorkbook.com
www.WritingWorkbook.com

ISBN print ed.	0-9725986-0-X
ISBN PDF download ed.	0-9725986-2-6

Printed in the United States of America
First Printing: November 2002
Second Printing: February 2003
Third Printing: December 2003
Fourth Printing: August 2004
Fifth Printing: August 2005
Sixth Printing: February 2007
Seventh Printing: January 2008
Eighth Printing: June 2009

Table of Contents
Clear, Correct, Concise E-Mail: A Writing Workbook for Customer Service Agents

Writing Practices

Writing Practices *(continued)*

Chapter 8—Put It All Together: Apply What You've Learned about Writing Customer Service E-Mail

Writing Tools

Introduction
How to Use the Writing *Workbook*

E-commerce has changed the way you hear from your customers. Increasingly, customers e-mail their questions and complaints and expect (quick!) e-mail responses. That means that writing is now an even more important skill for customer service agents. But your writing skills may be rusty. It's probably been a long time since your last English class. Or this may be the first time you've been required to write on the job. The *Workbook* is designed to help you polish your writing skills and to give you guidance and practice in writing good customer service e-mails.

What Is the *Workbook?*

For customer service agents, this *Workbook* is an ideal way to address different needs and writing skill levels. You can proceed at your own pace. Take the **Pre-Test** in **Chapter 2** to identify your strengths and weaknesses, then spend your time on those areas in which you need the most help.

If the word "grammar" takes you back to unpleasant memories of eighth grade English, don't despair. This *Workbook* is short on rules and long on practice. Do the e-mails in the **Practices** look like ones you answer every day? We hope so! All of the examples and **Practices** are adapted from actual customer service e-mails. (We've changed the names of companies, customers, and customer service agents. We've substituted fake URLs, phone numbers, and other contact information.)

You may be looking at this *Workbook* because your supervisor has advised you to strengthen your writing skills. Or perhaps your company is using the **Pre-Test** or **Competency Test** (available at www.WritingWorkbook.com) to assess your writing skills. You may be completing the *Workbook* to qualify for a new job. Whatever the reason, you'll find the *Workbook* an efficient way to refresh the writing skills you need as a customer service agent.

For Customer Service Agents—
How to Use the *Workbook* to Improve Job Skills

Use the *Workbook* to review basic writing skills. If you lack confidence in your writing skills, you may want to read all the guidance and do all the **Practices** in the *Workbook*.

Use the *Workbook* to focus on particular writing problems. Perhaps your grammar skills are strong, but you've never really understood how to use a comma correctly. You should go straight to **Chapter 6—Punctuate Correctly** and read the guidance and complete the comma **Practices** in that chapter.

What's in the *Workbook*?

We take the word *Workbook* seriously. That means this *Workbook* is **meant to be worked in.** The *Workbook* is full of **Practices.** We've provided room for you to write and lots of white space where you can scribble notes. Neatness doesn't count. Building strong writing skills does!

Writing Skills Review and Practice

Chapter 3, Chapter 4, Chapter 5, Chapter 6, and Chapter 7 focus on specific writing skills. Each chapter contains guidance, examples, and practice. Many of the chapters also contain lists, checklists, and other writing tools.

Skills Tests and a Wrap-Up Chapter

Chapter 2—Pre-Test: Assess Your Writing Skills will help you identify your writing strengths and the areas where you need help.

Chapter 8—Put It All Together gives you the opportunity to practice the writing skills you've learned by writing or editing complete messages.

Writing Resources

We're often asked for suggestions on writing resources, so we've listed our favorite print and online writing resources to answer your grammar, style, and usage questions. We've also listed some resources that will give you additional writing practice.

How Long Will It Take to Complete the *Workbook*?

How long it takes to complete the *Workbook* depends on how much of the *Workbook* you do. All told, you should be able to complete the entire *Workbook* in eight to ten hours. You say you don't have eight uninterrupted hours? Don't worry. The *Workbook* is structured so you can do it in short chunks—while commuting to work (assuming you're not driving!), during your lunch break, or during your child's soccer practice. Just pick up a pencil and work on your chosen chapter whenever you have time.

You may want to organize a group of friends or colleagues and do the *Workbook* together. Working in a group is fun, and you're more apt to do the **Practices** if you know your group is meeting.

For Managers—How to Use the *Workbook* to Improve Your Staff's Writing

The *Workbook* came about because we began hearing from companies about the difficulty of finding customer service agents with the writing skills needed to answer customers' e-mail. Some companies shifted telephone agents to e-mail and found that the agents' writing skills didn't match their product knowledge and phone skills. Other companies found that agents hired to write e-mail had rusty writing skills or were not experienced in business writing. Regardless of the situation, the *Workbook* offers the solution for getting customer service agents up to speed in the essential skills they'll need to write e-mail.

You can use this *Workbook* in several ways:

- Train agents who have the product knowledge but lack the writing skills to compose effective customer service e-mails.

- Help agents with weak writing skills improve their grammar and usage.

- Assess writing skills. Managers can use the **Pre-Test** to assess writing skills and the **Competency Exam** (available at www.WritingWorkbook.com) to certify agents in essential writing skills.

The *Workbook* is a flexible training tool that can suit almost any training situation:

- **For self-paced instruction.** Agents can complete the entire *Workbook* as a self-paced writing course. Or agents can take the **Pre-Test** in **Chapter 2** to identify the skills they need to improve and then complete only the relevant chapters and **Practices**. Agents can use the *Workbook* during work hours or at home.

- **As the basis for instructor-led training.** E-mail us at training@WritingWorkbook.com or call 877-481-1869 for information about our customized training programs for customer service agents.

- **For a group of agents working together to improve writing skills.** Groups provide peer support in completing the *Workbook*.

This *Workbook* is a perfect solution to the logistical problem managers face: freeing agents to attend a course on the same day (and leaving no one to respond to customers!).

Names Have Been Changed...

Before writing this *Workbook*, we collected hundreds of customer service e-mails—the good, the bad, the ugly. They helped us determine the *Workbook* content and provided the raw material, examples and **Practices**. However, as they say, "names have been changed." We've "cleansed" the e-mails, changing all identifiable information such as company and agent names, URLs, tracking numbers, phone numbers, and other contact information. To the best of our knowledge, all identifying information is fictitious.

E-Mail Writing Skills Competency Exam: A Companion to this Workbook

Many managers need a tool to help them assess the writing skills of agents or job applicants. We've developed the **E-Mail Writing Skills Competency Exam** for that purpose. Use the **Competency Exam** to evaluate agents' and applicants' e-mail writing skills—the skills taught in this *Workbook*.

Use the **Competency Exam** to

- assess current customer service agents' writing skills

- assess job applicants' writing skills before hiring them

- identify your staff's need for writing training

- certify customer service agents' e-mail writing competency

- test agents' writing proficiency and score their performance after they have completed the *Workbook*

Use the Competency Exam "Off the Shelf" or Customize It

The exam includes a writing exercise that requires the exam-taker to respond to a customer's e-mail. You can use our writing exercise, or you can customize the **Competency Exam** by substituting your own e-mail writing exercise. Whether you use the test "as is" or customize it, the **Scoring Checklist** will help you to score the writing exercise.

Order the Competency Exam at the *Workbook* Web site: WritingWorkbook.com.

More Information on E-Mail Writing at www.WritingWorkbook.com

Visit us online for more information about writing e-mail to customers. The Web site contains additional materials to supplement the *Workbook.* You'll find two printable certificates to download:

- A *Certificate of Completion* you can award to agents who successfully complete the *Workbook*

- A *Competency Certificate* you can award to agents who pass the **E-Mail Writing Skills Competency Exam**

You'll also find articles related to customer service e-mail. Check our Web site frequently for new articles and companion materials.

About the Authors and E-WRITE

When we started our writing training and consulting company in 1996, e-mail was in its infancy and the Internet still a techie toy. But we were so convinced of the power of online communication that we boldly named our company **E-WRITE**. Since then, we've worked with organizations of every size and type, teaching them to improve their e-mail communications and create user-focused web content.

We've customized our courses and workshops for Fortune 500 companies, Internet start-ups, federal and local governments, and nonprofits. We've developed courses and workshops for American Airlines, Coca-Cola, Fannie Mae, Prudential, Humana, The College Board, Key Bank, Pan American Health Organization, the U.S. Air Force, FedWeb, and The National Wildlife Foundation. Participants in our courses and workshops include high-level executives, marketing teams, and web teams as well as customer service agents.

We have a special interest in teaching writing to the front line administrative and support personnel who communicate with customers directly, every day. We believe that writing is a teachable skill and that good writers are made, not born. Our approach to writing training is practical and hands-on. We've found that people learn best and are most receptive when the training focuses on the skills they need to do their job. We've drawn on that philosophy and experience in developing this *Workbook.*

We've written extensively on e-mail and online writing. Our articles appear in our e-mail newsletter, **The E-Writing Bulletin,** and in numerous online publications, magazines and newsletters. We've written web content and e-mail marketing materials for Sallie Mae; NIH's National Human Genome Research Institute; the Smithsonian Institution's National Air and Space Museum and National Museum of American History; OvationTV; the Consumer Electronics Show; WebSmart Kids; the Appalachian Regional Commission; Adoptions Together; and Eco-Artware.com, among others.

How To Contact Us

Marilynne Rudick

Marilynne@WritingWorkbook.com

Telephone: 877–481–1869 or 301–986–9627

Leslie O'Flahavan

Leslie@WritingWorkbook.com

Telephone: 301–989–9583

Write to us at

E-WRITE
407 Scott Drive
Silver Spring, MD 20904

Fax us at
301–718–8021

Thanks to Those Who Helped Us

We are grateful to many people who helped us with this workbook. Special thanks to Dick Hannus, Hannus Design; Janice Sterling; Tanya Renne, Renne Development; Amanda Patton; Cindy Leitner; Jill Groce; Jen McClure and Elizabeth Albrycht, Albrycht, McClure &Partners. Many thanks to Brenda Davenport whose enthusiastic response to early drafts, and help along the way, carried us to completion.

We are especially thankful for our *Workbook* testers. Heather Brown, Gaelon Farquharson, Tana Scoby-Hubbard, and Charlot McKinney, customer service agents extraordinaire, tested the *Workbook* cover-to-cover. Their comments and feedback were invaluable and greatly contributed to making the *Workbook* a better product. Our thanks as well to Pat Seidel, Connie Pierre-pont, Pat Dreyer, Rochelle Kramer, Karen Cagungun, and Sharon Willier who tested and provided feedback on individual *Workbook* chapters. We appreciate the editorial and marketing expertise of Pat McNees, Fran Simon, Peggy Van Hulsteyn, and Debbie Weil.

And a special measure of thanks to our families—Bob Sher, John O'Flahavan, Linnae O'Flahavan, Paige O'Flahavan, and Barrie Miller—whose support goes far beyond this *Workbook*.

How to Buy *Clear, Correct, Concise E-Mail: A Writing Workbook for Customer Service Agents*

Like Starbucks' infinite variations on coffee, this *Workbook* is available in a variety of formats: **print or PDF download.** You also can purchase a **license** for multiple copies at a substantially reduced price.

To buy the **print version** of the *Workbook:*

• Use the order form at the end of the *Workbook*

• Order online at www.WritingWorkbook.com

• Order by phone: 877–481–1869

• Fax your order: 301–718–8021

To purchase the *Workbook* as a **PDF Download**, go to www.WritingWorkbook.com.

For information about licensing the *Workbook*, phone us at 877–481–1869 or e-mail us at info@WritingWorkbook.com.

"I'd like to train my entire staff. Can I copy and distribute *Workbook* materials?"

We're pleased that you'd like to train your entire staff, but you can't copy and distribute *Workbook* materials. The *Workbook*, **Competency Exam**, and related training products are copyright protected. That means you can't copy or use information from *Clear, Correct, Concise E-Mail* or the **Competency Exam** without written permission from us—*even if you credit us as the source.* Using our training products without our permission is copyright infringement and is illegal. We do on occasion give permission to organizations or individuals to use guidance or Practices without charge, but in most instances, *if you'd like to train a group of people, you'll need to purchase copies or licenses for each person.*

The good news is that we offer bulk rates on print copies of the **Workbook** and **Competency Exam** and sell licenses to our training products at substantially reduced rates. You can see our bulk pricing at http://www.WritingWorkbook.com/buy/bulk.html.

So, if you're training a group of agents—or your entire staff—your best bet is to contact us. We'll help you figure out how to buy print copies or license the product at the lowest cost. And we'll be glad to provide you plenty of advice on how to use the training products successfully. (Our advice is free!)

Chapter 1
What Makes a Great Customer Service E-Mail?

Most of this Workbook is about how you can improve your customer service e-mail writing skills. But before we start explaining how to fix writing problems in e-mail, let's discuss the writing traits we think make a message great.

Read an Example of Great Customer Service E-Mail Writing

What makes a great customer service e-mail? The answer may seem obvious. Great customer service e-mail answers the customer's question. But answering a customer's question clearly, correctly, concisely, and professionally can be a real challenge!

Do you want to read an example of excellent customer service e-mail? Read this exchange between a customer, Laura Anderson, and customer service agent Kara Zorn at Cottage Style, which is both an online and a bricks-and-mortar clothing retailer.

Customer's E-Mail

To:	customerservice@cottagestyle.com
From:	laura@earthnet.com
Subject:	Pants, size 6?
Date:	5/10/05 10:32 AM

I purchased a pair of pants, size 8, at the Stonefield, VA outlet store. I'd like to exchange them for a smaller size. I've been told that no size 6 pants are available. I'm wondering whether the pants come in petite sizes and whether a size 6 petite is available.

The item number is 031020581 -- side-zip, elastic-back pants, in olive green.

Can I machine wash these pants?

Thanks --

Laura Anderson

Customer Service Agent's Response

> **To:** laura@earthnet.com
> **From:** customerservice@cottagestyle.com
> **Subject:** Response to your question about petite size pants from Cottage Style
> **Date:** 5/10/05   14:07 PM
>
> Dear Ms. Anderson,
>
> Thank you for contacting us about the pair of pants you purchased from our Stonefield outlet store. You asked whether the pants you purchased came in a petite size 6. We checked on the sizes available and are sorry that these pants never came in petite sizes. However, there are a couple of size 4 pants available. The waist measurement is 25.5 inches and the hip measurement is 39 inches.
>
> If you would like to try the size 4 pants, please package the pants you now have. Mail them to Cottage Style Returns Department, 101 Cottage Style Drive, Laramie, Wyoming 82070. Be sure to include a note in the package with your name and address. In the note, indicate in large red letters that you would like to exchange the pants for a size 4. If you decide to try the size 4, please do this right away. We have only a few pairs left.
>
> We will be happy to process your exchange as soon as we receive the size 8 pants. There's no additional charge for this exchange.
>
> As for how to care for these pants, the cleaning instructions advise dry cleaning.
>
> If we may be of further assistance, please contact us by e-mail at customerservice@cottagestyle.com or phone us at 800-510-2808 between 8 a.m. and 6 p.m. Eastern Standard Time.
>
> We appreciate your business!
>
> Sincerely,
>
> Kara Zorn
> *Internet Customer Service*

Find Ten Ways the Customer Service Agent's Response Is an Example of Great Writing

Now that you've read agent Kara Zorn's response, it's your turn! In the space below, list at least ten ways this response is an example of great customer service writing. Or you may circle ten excellent traits of Kara Zorn's response, marking the message on page 10. When you've found ten traits of great writing, compare your list with our list and explanations beginning on page 13.

1. _____

2. _____

3. _____

4. _____

5. _____

6. _____

7. _____

8. _____

9. _____

10. _____

Customer Service Agent's Response

Use a helpful subject line

To: laura@earthnet.com
From: customerservice@cottagestyle.com
Subject: Response to your question about petite size pants from Cottage Style
Date: 5/10/05   14:07 PM

Respond promptly

Personalize the response

Dear Ms. Anderson,

Use a personal tone

Answer the customer's question

Thank you for contacting us about the pair of pants you purchased from our Stonefield outlet store. You asked whether the pants you purchased came in a petite size 6. We checked on the sizes available and are sorry that these pants never came in petite sizes. However, there are a couple of size 4 pants available. The waist measurement is 25.5 inches and the hip measurement is 39 inches.

Try to solve the customer's problem

Make it possible for the customer to take action

If you would like to try the size 4 pants, please package the pants you now have. Mail them to Cottage Style Returns Department, 101 Cottage Style Drive, Laramie, Wyoming 82070. Be sure to include a note in the package with your name and address. In the note, indicate in large red letters that you would like to exchange the pants for a size 4. If you decide to try the size 4, please do this right away. We have only a few pairs left.

Use a polite, positive tone

We will be happy to process your exchange as soon as we receive the size 8 pants. There's no additional charge for this exchange.

Answer the customer's question

As for how to care for these pants, the cleaning instructions advise dry cleaning.

If we may be of further assistance, please contact us by e-mail or phone us at 800-510-2808 between 8 a.m. and 6 p.m. Eastern Standard Time.

Use a polite, positive tone

We appreciate your business!

Sincerely,

Close the message with your name

Kara Zorn
Internet Customer Service

Make it easy for the customer to contact you

Ten Ways Kara Zorn's Response Is an Example of Great Writing

Here's our list of ten ways this is an example of great customer service e-mail writing. Compare our list with your list. Do they match?

1. Use a helpful subject line.

The agent wrote a clear and useful subject line. The subject line helps the customer know right away that the message is a response to her question. A subject line such as *Re: 031020581* does not tell the customer what the e-mail is about. Even worse, it makes the customer feel like a number, not a valued customer. Unhelpful subject lines get lost in e-mail boxes and often get mistaken for spam and deleted. But this subject line, *Response to your question about petite size pants from Cottage Style,* will get the customer's attention and help solve her problem.

2. Respond promptly.

Cottage Style responded promptly. The e-mail received at 10:32 a.m. was answered that afternoon at 2:07 p.m. Because e-mail messages can be sent instantly, customers expect a fast response.

3. Personalize the response.

A customer who has taken the time to write an e-mail deserves to be treated as a person, not a number. This e-mail response addresses the customer by name: *Dear Ms. Anderson.* The opening paragraph personalizes the response by repeating information in the customer's e-mail: she shopped at the company's Stonefield outlet store. Finally, a person with a name, Kara Zorn, signed the message, not the anonymous Customer Service Department.

4. Answer all the customer's questions.

The customer asked Cottage Style two questions:

- In the first paragraph, she asked, *Is a size 6 petite available?*
- In the third paragraph, she asked, *Can I machine wash these pants?*

The agent answered the first question in the first paragraph. She wrote, *We checked on the sizes available and are sorry that these pants never came in petite sizes.* She answered the second question in the fourth paragraph: *As for how to care for these pants, the cleaning instructions advise dry cleaning.*

How is answering the customer's question a trait of excellent customer service e-mail? Shouldn't all customer service e-mail answer customers' questions? Well, it should, but too often it doesn't. Sometimes the agent replies to the customer but doesn't answer the question. Particularly annoying are responses that send the customer back to the Web site or to a catalog. Most likely, the customer couldn't find the answer there in the first place.

5. Make it possible for the customer to take action.

If the customer can or should do something after reading the customer service agent's response, make sure the e-mail includes the information needed to take action. In this e-mail, the agent invites Laura to return the size 8 pants and try the size 4 pants. She gives Laura all the information needed to complete the transaction. She writes:

> *If you would like to try the size 4 pants, please package the pants you now have. Mail them to Cottage Style Returns Department, 101 Cottage Style Drive, Laramie, Wyoming 82070. Be sure to include a note in the package with your name and address. In the note, indicate in large red letters that you would like a size exchange for a size 4.*

The agent doesn't merely send Laura to the Cottage Style Web site for information on how to exchange a purchase.

6. Solve the customer's problem.

Solving the customer's problem involves more than merely answering the customer's question. And solving the customer's problem is the gold standard of customer service by e-mail or any other method. In Cottage Style's response, the agent answers the question about availability of size 6 petite pants by telling her the pants don't come in petite sizes. She then tries to solve the problem by suggesting that a size 4 might fit. She gives the measurements so the customer can decide whether the size 4 will fit. Then the agent explains exactly how to make an exchange.

7. Use a polite, positive, and personal tone.

The agent writes in a tone that lets Laura know the company values her and wants to keep her as a customer, using phrases such as *We will be happy to process your exchange* and *We appreciate your business!* that contribute to the e-mail's polite, positive, and personal tone.

8. Write clearly and simply.

This e-mail is easy to read and understand. Take a look at the second paragraph. The sentences are short and concise. They are written in the active voice, which emphasizes what the customer should do and what the company will do.

The e-mail is free of jargon, confusing idioms, and regional expressions. This makes it easy to understand, even if the customer's native language isn't English.

9. Proofread for mechanical errors.

This e-mail response contains no spelling, punctuation, or grammatical errors. Imagine that the agent's first draft contained two "word" errors. Perhaps she incorrectly wrote **pare** *of pants* instead of **pair** *of pants*. Perhaps, in the fourth paragraph, she incorrectly wrote *the cleaning instructions* **advice** *dry cleaning* instead of **advise**. Luckily, the agent took the time to proofread the e-mail before she sent it. She caught any errors she might have made with "look-alike" words that can slip through a spell-checker program.

Mechanical errors give the impression that the company is careless, the customer service agent is in too much of a rush to take the time for a careful response, and the company does not care very much about the customer. Mechanical correctness shows you care enough to proofread.

10. Make it easy for the customer to contact you.

The Cottage Style agent included a phone number so the customer has an alternate way of contacting the company if she has further questions, if the problem is not solved, or if her e-mail system is down! The agent lets the customer know the customer service department's hours and gives the time zone.

Checklist: Ten Traits of a Great Customer Service E-Mail

Would you like to make sure all of your customer service e-mails are great? Use this Checklist when responding to your customer's e-mail queries.

1. Use a helpful subject line.

2. Respond promptly.

3. Personalize the response.

4. Answer all the customer's questions.

5. Make it possible for the customer to take action.

6. Solve the customer's problem.

7. Use a polite, positive, and personal tone.

8. Write clearly and simply.

9. Proofread for mechanical errors.

10. Make it easy for the customer to contact you.

Chapter 2
Pre-Test: Assess Your Writing Skills

*Complete the **Pre-Test** before you begin the **Workbook**. You'll find out what you know and what you need to learn.*

About the Pre-Test

The **Pre-Test** has 14 sections. Each section has five questions. Do the entire **Pre-Test**. If you're not sure of an answer, just give it a try. Your **Pre-Test** won't be "scored." Instead, this test will help you decide how best to use the *Workbook*.

When you've completed the **Pre-Test**, compare your answers with those on pages 29 through 41. If you got all five questions in a section correct, you don't need to spend much time on that area. If you get one or more items wrong in any section of the **Pre-Test**, you should read the corresponding *Workbook* section or chapter and do the **Practices**.

Good luck!

Section I—Change Passive Voice to Active Voice

Rewrite the sentences below to change passive voice to active voice. Active voice means that the subject of the sentence "does" the action in the sentence.

1. The card can be used by shoppers to purchase goods online or at our retail location.

2. A receipt will be sent to you by our sales representative after we receive your payment.

3. A disruption in your cable service has been caused by road construction in your area.

4. The invoice number should be included by you in all your correspondence with us.

5. The instructions on how to register for Soccer Camp can be found on the left side of the Summer 2005 page at our Web site.

How did you do on Section I? Compare your answers with those on page 29. If you got any of the five items wrong, be sure to review the topic and complete the active voice **Practices** in **Chapter 3—Write Clear, Strong Sentences.**

Section II—Revise to Remove Confusion Caused by Misplaced or Dangling Modifiers

Rewrite the sentences to eliminate the confusion caused by misplaced or dangling modifiers. Modifiers are words that add information or details in a sentence. They belong close to the word or phrase they modify. Misplaced modifiers appear in the wrong place and confuse the meaning of the sentence. Dangling modifiers are words or phrases that modify a word not clearly stated in the sentence.

1. Some investors nearly spend all their money trading stocks online.

2. The supplier said that the new, solar-powered model would be ready soon at the press conference last week.

3. While enrolled in our high-volume sales program, the company will give you first chance at new releases and new products.

4. Under the reservation schedule we established last year, we are only allowed to lease this beach-front condominium for one week at a time.

5. Too slow, too old, or lacking the software you want, we can offer you the computer you've always wanted at low, low prices.

How did you do on Section II? Compare your answers with those on page 30. If you got any of the five items wrong, be sure to review the topic and complete the modifier **Practices** in **Chapter 3—Write Clear, Strong Sentences.**

Section III—Change Fragments into Full Sentences

Rewrite the sentences below to change fragments into full sentences. A fragment is a group of words—a phrase or a dependent clause—but not a complete sentence, which has a subject and a verb.

1. Signing you up for our referral service.

2. Or, if the delivery should go to an address other than the billing address.

3. If there hasn't been an update to your credit report.

4. Being submitted to the search engine.

5. Because we have found another service provider.

How did you do on Section III? Compare your answers with those on page 31. If you got any of the five items wrong, be sure to review the topic and complete the sentence fragment **Practices** in **Chapter 3— Write Clear, Strong Sentences.**

Section IV—Change Run-Ons into Full Sentences

Rewrite the sentences below to change run-ons into full sentences. Run-ons are two or more sentences linked by incorrect punctuation.

1. Currently we do not have a designated service agent for our children's products, we suggest that you contact our general customer service group at 800-555-9131.

2. Insurance advisors are available at three locations in each county, we guarantee you will be able to see an advisor at any one of these locations.

3. Thank you for contacting us about the antique mirror you would like to sell, I am not sure whether our buyer will be interested in it, but I will tell her about your mirror.

4. The digital camera is portable and durable it would be a great choice for a long backpacking trip.

5. This is in response to your e-mail asking whether we provide security services for outdoor concerts we do not but we can recommend another company if you are interested.

How did you do on Section IV? Compare your answers with those on page 31. If you got any of the five items wrong, be sure to review the topic and complete the run-on sentence **Practices** in **Chapter 3—Write Clear, Strong Sentences.**

Section V—Replace Weak Verbs with Strong Verbs

Rewrite the sentences below to replace weak verbs with strong verbs. Weak verbs make your writing less forceful. Using strong, active verbs instead of the verb *to be* will improve your writing.

1. You can conduct a review of our references or you can make contact with the clients who are listed on the attachment to this memo.

2. It is a good idea to think about buying commercial-quality carpeting from a licensed dealer.

3. There are lots of different ways for amateur beer makers to begin to brew beer at home.

4. At our Web site it is possible to make a calculation of your mortgage payment at various interest rates.

5. The new American Museum of Regional Art has been working on collecting three large murals by a little-known artist who worked in Arkansas in the 1950s.

How did you do on Section V? Compare your answers with those on page 32. If you got any of the five items wrong, be sure to review the topic and complete the **Practices** on replacing weak verbs in **Chapter 3—Write Clear, Strong Sentences.**

The tone of this message from agent Joshua Manning to customer Mr. Lee is inappropriate; it's bureaucratic and angry. Circle the words or phrases in this e-mail that give it an unfriendly tone.

To: Leeman@CDColl.com
From: Jmanning@YourE-host.com
Subject: Overdue payment

Dear Mr. Lee,

This is to inform you that our records indicate that your payment for Internet service is more than 60 days overdue. Because you haven't responded to our repeated letters and phone calls, we have no choice but to discontinue your service if we do not receive your payment within five business days. Termination is per our signed agreement.

In the event that you would like us to continue to be your Internet service provider, we must receive payment on or before January 3, 2005. If not, we will terminate your service as of that date. We are not in business to provide service for free.

Perhaps you need to review your accounting system?

Joshua Manning
Account Manager

How did you do on Section VI? Compare your answers with those on page 34. If you missed any, be sure to review the topic and complete the **Practices** in **Chapter 4—Write With a Polite, Positive, and Personal Tone.**

Spelling mistakes happen when you misspell a word, make a typo, or choose a look-alike or sound-alike word instead of the correct word. Circle the misspelled or incorrect words in this e-mail from agent Robert Cardon. Write your correction in the space above the incorrect word.

To: JillJennings@msn.com
From: Robert.Cardon@Bagsbeyond.com
Subject: Re: Question about Weekender Tote

Hi, Jill!

Thank you for your e-mail about our Weekender Tote Bag. The tote is 36 inches long. The total wait is three pounds. It has duel compartments and a handy side zipper, which is convenient for papers or jewlry. It can accomodate clothes for an entire weekend. The hole tote bag is completely handmaid from 100 percent cotton fabrick. The seems are reinforced for long life. The tote is currently on sail for $39.95. You can order it threw our catelog or online.

The tote is guaranted for too years. I'm sure you will recieve many years of service from it.

Robert Cardon
Customer Care Agent

How did you do on Section VII? Compare your answers with those on page 35. Did you find all 15 errors? If you missed any, be sure to review the topic and complete the **Practices** in **Chapter 5—Select the Correct Word and Spell It Right.**

Section VIII—Use the Period Correctly

Add periods to these sentences.

1. Check the name of each school where you want us to send your financial aid form (You may select up to ten schools)

2. We will be happy to address your questions about your bill

3. After about five minutes of idle time, my connection was terminated because of a "time out"

4. Our knowledgeable technicians will install unlimited software upgrades at your home or office

5. Our customer service hours are 9 a m to 5 p m

How did you do on Section VIII? Compare your answers with those on page 35. If you got any of the five items wrong, be sure to review the topic and complete the period **Practices** in **Chapter 6—Punctuate Correctly.**

Section IX—Use the Comma Correctly

Add commas to these sentences.

1. We have also opened corporate offices in Chicago Los Angeles and Seattle.

2. At any rate we can supply temporary staff if you decide to add personnel for this short-term project.

3. To apply for government drought-relief funds you must complete the H39 Form which establishes the dollar value of your crop loss then send the H39 to the address at the bottom of the form.

4. I want to return the end table I bought but I don't have the receipt anymore.

5. You replaced your 1997 model with the 2005 model Freda and probably saved $150 per year in operating costs.

How did you do on Section IX? Compare your answers with those on page 36. If you got any of the five items wrong, be sure to review the topic and complete the comma **Practices** in **Chapter 6—Punctuate Correctly.**

Section X—Use the Apostrophe Correctly

Add apostrophes to these sentences.

1. The beneficiarys name is Patricia Arisa.

2. With Dercks enhanced service contract, you will avoid maintenance fees for almost 3 years.

3. I havent bought college textbooks on the Web since I began graduate school.

4. The College Mens Intramural Sports Program is funded by alumni donations, and the College Womens Intramural Sports Program is funded by a private foundation.

5. When cleaning the bag attachment, its best to grasp the Weed Trimmer by its plastic handle, not the bag clip.

   How did you do on Section X? Compare your answers with those on page 37. If you got any of the five items wrong, be sure to review the topic and complete the apostrophe **Practices** in **Chapter 6—Punctuate Correctly.**

Section XI—Use the Semicolon Correctly

Add semicolons to these sentences.

1. Many customers are interested in the lowest price however, that price may not buy the best product.

2. You may be interested in these vacation rental properties: our two-bedroom, two-bathroom condo in Fort Lauderdale our rustic mountain cabin in the Allegheny Mountains or our three-bedroom, two-bathroom beach house on Cape Cod.

3. Hosts Laura and Mitchell Brooks are a fascinating couple I can promise you'll arrive as guests and you'll leave as friends.

4. If you're interested in earning your GED online, please contact James Hoyt, registrar Muriel Worden, student counselor and Brian Bundocks, instructor.

5. We will resolve the problems you have had getting the books delivered we can send the materials by FedEx or by courier.

How did you do on Section XI? Compare your answers with those on page 38. If you got any of the five items wrong, be sure to review the topic and complete the semicolon **Practices** in **Chapter 6—Punctuate Correctly.**

Section XII—Use the Colon Correctly

Add colons to these sentences.

1. We are open during traditional business hours 10:00 a.m. until 7:30 p.m., Monday through Friday.

2. We'll give you all the tourist information you'll need to have a great trip what sights to see, where to eat, what to do, and which local tour companies to use.

3. We have two pricing plans an annual fee of $295.00 or a monthly fee of $29.95.

4. Our telephone agent reports that customers are pleased with the new design of the monthly statement she received five positive phone calls about the statement on Monday morning alone.

5. The following periodicals are published monthly *Burning Tree Anthology, Words Work,* and *The Special Writer.*

How did you do on Section XII? Compare your answers with those on page 39. If you got any of the five items wrong, be sure to review the topic and complete the colon **Practices** in **Chapter 6—Punctuate Correctly.**

Write *C* next to the sentences that are punctuated correctly. Write *I* next to the sentences that are punctuated incorrectly.

	1.	Each of the products registered on our system has a $5, shipping and handling charge.
	2.	Also, if you have a problem with another purchase (and we would hope you would not), please let the store manager know.
	3.	You should go to our website: www.paulbfoods.com and click on the Products menu.
	4.	I'm giving you two price quotes for the 16-night cruise you inquired about, Lorri; and I hope you'll contact me soon to reserve a stateroom.
	5.	Home improvement loans are not subsidized by the federal government; therefore, applicants do not have to fill out the HL-619 Form.
	6.	Take a steam locomotive trip in Maryland's scenic Allegheny Mountains and enjoy a bit of our region's past.
	7.	Your total of $26.84 will be charged to your credit card (please note that this charge will appear on your credit card statement from LITTLE IVAN ENTERPRISES).
	8.	To sell an item, access it's detail page on our web site and click on the Sell button at the upper right corner of the screen.
	9.	All our woodworking tools are backed by our Product Promise: if you are not entirely satisfied with a tool, return it to us at any time for an exchange or a refund of its purchase price.
	10.	This message is being sent by the Confidence.com autoresponder, so no live person will see your reply.

How did you do on Section XIII? Compare your answers with those on page 40. If you got any of the 10 items wrong, be sure to review the topic and complete the punctuation **Practices** in **Chapter 6—Punctuate Correctly.**

This message to Mr. Sullivan from agent Sandy includes idioms, gender-biased words, and other words or phrases that could confuse non-native English speakers. Circle the words or phrases global customers might not understand.

To: Gsullivan@wdesw.org
From: sandy@cedarcr.com
Subject: Re: Cedar Crest online pricing

Dear Mr. Sullivan,

Thanks for getting in touch with Cedar Crest about prices. I'm Sandy, the salesman in charge of customer service. We appreciate your interest in purchasing fine wood products from us.

The products, prices, and promotions in our retail craft stores will sometimes differ from those offered online. As a rule, our retail stores don't have the capability to match online prices and vice versa. That capability is in the works and we hope to have it up and running soon. Your best bet is to phone the retail store ahead of time and tell the salesman which products you are interested in -- woodworking tools, books, or fine craft gift items -- and give him the Internet prices. He will match those prices if the Internet prices are lower than the store prices.

Have you seen our latest Super Stuff bargains? We're selling everything from rocking chairs to greeting cards. You need more Super Stuff! To make sure you are up to speed, go to www.cedarcr.com/stuff. New offers are added all day long, so don't be a stranger!

We look forward to your next visit to one of our Cedar Crest stores or to www.cedarcr.com. In the bricks-and-mortar world, we're open from 9:30 a.m. until 9:30 p.m.

Best wishes,
Sandy and the Customer Care Team

How did you do on Section XIV? Compare your answers with those on page 41. If you missed any, be sure to review the topic and complete the **Practices** in **Chapter 7—Write For Global Customers**.

Pre-Test Answers

Compare your **Pre-Test** answers with those below. If you answered all five questions correctly in a section, you probably do not need to study all the **Practices** in the corresponding *Workbook* chapter or section. If you made one or more errors in any section of this **Pre-Test**, you should read the guidance and do the **Practice** in that skill area.

Answers to Section I—Change Passive Voice to Active Voice

Go to **Chapter 3—Write Clear, Strong Sentences**, page 43, to review and practice writing in the active voice. You'll learn how to write sentences in the active voice and learn why your customers prefer active voice sentences.

1. *Passive*   The card can be used by shoppers to purchase goods online or at our retail location.

   Active   Shoppers can use the card to purchase goods online or at our retail location.

2. *Passive*   A receipt will be sent to you by our sales representative after we receive your payment.

   Active   Our sales representative will send you a receipt after we receive your payment.

3. *Passive*   A disruption in your cable service has been caused by road construction in your area.

   Active   Road construction in your area has caused a disruption in your cable service.

4. *Passive*   The invoice number should be included by you in all your correspondence with us.

   Active   You should include the invoice number in all your correspondence with us.

5. *Passive*   The instructions on how to register for Soccer Camp can be found on the left side of the Summer 2005 page at our Web site.

   Active   You can find instructions on how to register for Soccer Camp on the left side of the Summer 2005 page at our Web site.

Go to **Chapter 3—Write Clear, Strong Sentences**, page 47, to review and practice how to place modifiers in sentences so the meaning will be clear. You'll learn how a misplaced or dangling modifier can make a sentence confusing, even humorous, and how to correct modifier errors. The modifier in each sentence appears in **bold** type, so you can easily recognize it and see where it was moved to clarify the sentence.

1. *Misplaced Modifier*   Some investors **nearly** spend all their money trading stocks online.

   Corrected Modifier   Some investors spend **nearly** all their money trading stocks online.

2. *Misplaced Modifier*   The supplier said that the new, solar-powered model would be ready soon **at the press conference last week.**

   Corrected Modifier   **At the press conference last week,** the supplier said that the new, solar-powered model would be ready soon.

3. *Misplaced modifier*   **While enrolled in our high-volume** sales program, the company will give you first chance at new releases and new products.

   Corrected Modifier   The company will give you first chance at new releases and new products **while you are enrolled in our high-volume sales program.**

4. *Misplaced Modifier*   Under the reservation schedule we established last year, we are **only** allowed to lease this beach-front condominium for one week at a time.

   Corrected Modifier   Under the reservation schedule we established last year, we are allowed to lease this beach-front condominium for **only** one week at a time.

5. *Dangling Modifier*   **Too slow, too old, or lacking the software you want,** we can offer you the computer you've always wanted at low, low prices.

   Corrected Modifier   If your computer is **too slow, too old, or lacking the software you want,** we can offer you the computer you've always wanted at low, low prices.

Answers to Section III—Change Fragments into Full Sentences

Go to **Chapter 3—Write Clear, Strong Sentences**, page 50, to review and practice writing full sentences. You'll learn how to identify and correct sentence fragments. Your answers may be different from these because you can fix sentence fragments more than one way.

1. *Fragment*   Signing you up for our referral service.

   Full Sentence   **We will** sign you up for our referral service.

2. *Fragment*   Or, if the delivery should go to an address other than the billing address.

   Full Sentence   **Please indicate on the form** if the delivery should go to an address other than the billing address.

3. *Fragment*   If there hasn't been an update to your credit report.

   Full Sentence   **You may submit last year's rental application** if there hasn't been an update to your credit report.

4. *Fragment*   Being submitted to the search engine.

   Full Sentence   Being submitted to the search engine **doesn't guarantee that a Web site will be popular.**

5. *Fragment*   Because we have found another service provider.

   Full Sentence   **Because we have found another service provider,** we will not renew our contract with your company.

Answers to Section IV—Change Run-ons into Full Sentences

Go to **Chapter 3—Write Clear, Strong Sentences**, page 53, to review and practice writing full sentences. You'll learn how to identify and correct run-on sentences. Your answers may be different from these because you can fix run-on sentences more than one way.

1. *Run-On*   Currently we do not have a designated service agent for our children's products, we suggest that you contact our general customer service group at 800–555–9131.

   Correct Sentence(s) Currently we do not have a designated service agent for our children's products. We suggest that you contact our general customer service group at 800–555–9131.

2. *Run-On*   Insurance advisors are available at three locations in each county, we guarantee you will be able to see an advisor at any one of these locations.

Correct Sentence(s)	Insurance advisors are available at three locations in each county; we guarantee you will be able to see an advisor at any one of these locations.
3. *Run-On*	Thank you for contacting us about the antique mirror you would like to sell, I am not sure whether our buyer will be interested in it, but I will tell her about your mirror.
Correct Sentence(s)	Thank you for contacting us about the antique mirror you would like to sell. I am not sure whether our buyer will be interested in it, but I will tell her about your mirror.
4. *Run-on*	The digital camera is portable and durable it would be a great choice for a long backpacking trip.
Correct Sentence(s)	The digital camera is portable and durable. It would be a great choice for a long backpacking trip.

—or—

	The digital camera is portable and durable, so it would be a great choice for a long backpacking trip.
5. *Run-on*	This is in response to your e-mail asking whether we provide security services for outdoor concerts we do not but we can recommend another company if you are interested.
Correct Sentence(s)	This is in response to your e-mail asking whether we provide security services for outdoor concerts. We do not, but we can recommend another company if you are interested.

Answers to Section V—Replace Weak Verbs with Strong Verbs

Go to **Chapter 3—Write Clear, Strong Sentences**, page 56, to review the topic and practice using strong verbs. You'll learn how to identify weak verbs and replace them with more forceful verbs. Your answers may be different from these, because you can correct weak verbs more than one way. However, be sure you identified the same weak verbs that we did.

1. *Weak Verbs*	You **can conduct a review** of our references, or you **can make contact** with our clients who are listed on the attachment to this memo.
Strong Verbs	You **can review** our references, or you **can contact** our clients who are listed on the attachment to this memo.

2. *Weak Verbs*

It i**s a good idea to think** about buying commercial-quality carpeting from a licensed dealer.

Strong Verbs

Think about buying commercial-quality carpeting from a licensed dealer.

3. *Weak Verbs*

There **are** lots of different ways for amateur beer makers **to begin to brew** beer at home.

Strong Verbs

Amateur beer makers **can try** several ways to **brew** beer at home.

4. *Weak Verbs*

At our Web site **it is possible to make a calculation** of your mortgage payment at various interest rates.

Strong Verbs

At our Web site you **can calculate** your mortgage payment at various interest rates.

5. *Weak Verbs*

The New American Museum of Regional Art **has been working on acquiring** three large paintings by a little-known muralist.

Strong verbs

The New American Museum of Regional Art **is acquiring** three large paintings by a little-known muralist.

Go to **Chapter 4—Write with a Polite, Positive, and Personal Tone**, page 65, to review and practice improving the tone of your writing. You'll learn about words and phrases that create tone and why the tone of your message is as important as the content.

The words or phrases that give this message an unfriendly tone appear in **bold** type. Did you identify the same words and phrases we did?

To: Leeman@CDColl.com
From: Jmanning@YourE-host.com
Subject: Overdue payment

Dear Mr. Lee,

This is to inform you that **our records indicate** that your payment for Internet service is more than 60 days overdue. Because you haven't **responded to our repeated letters and phone calls, we have no choice** but to discontinue your service if we do not receive your payment within five business days. **Termination is per our signed agreement**.

In the event that you would like to us to continue to be your Internet service provider, **we must receive payment on or before January 3, 2005.** If not, we will terminate your service as of that date. **We are not in business to provide service for free.**

Perhaps you need to review your accounting system?

Joshua Manning
Account Manager

Answers to Section VII—Select the Correct Word and Spell It Right

Go to **Chapter 5—Select the Correct Word and Spell It Right**, page 89, to review and practice spelling. You'll learn how to improve your spelling and how to distinguish between confusing sound-alike and look-alike words.

Did you find the 15 misspelled words in this e-mail message? The correct spellings appear in **bold** type.

To: JillJennings@msn.com
From: Robert.Cardon@Bagsbeyond.com
Subject: Re: Question about Weekender Tote

Hi, Jill!

Thank you for your e-mail about our Weekender Tote Bag. The tote is 36 inches long. The total **weight** is three pounds. It has **dual** compartments and a handy side zipper, which is convenient for papers or **jewelry**. It can **accommodate** clothes for an entire weekend. The **whole** tote bag is completely **handmade** from 100 percent cotton **fabric**. The **seams** are reinforced for long life. The tote is **currently** on **sale** for $39.95. You can order it **through** our **catalog** or online.

The tote is **guaranteed** for **two** years. I'm sure you will **receive** many years of service from it.

Robert Cardon
Customer Care Agent

Answers to Section VIII—Use the Period Correctly

Go to **Chapter 6—Punctuate Correctly**, page 106, to review and practice using the period correctly. You'll learn how to use the period in abbreviations and to punctuate sentences.

1. *Original*   Check the name of each school where you want us to send your financial aid form (You may select up to ten schools)

   Correct Sentences   Check the name of each school where you want us to send your financial aid form**.** (You may select up to ten schools**.**)

2. *Original*   We will be happy to address your questions about your bill

   Correct Sentence   We will be happy to address your questions about your bill**.**

3. *Original* After about five minutes of idle time, my connection was terminated because of a "time out"

   Correct Sentence After about five minutes of idle time, my connection was terminated because of a "time out."

4. *Original* Our knowledgeable technicians will install unlimited software upgrades at your home or office

   Correct Sentence Our knowledgeable technicians will install unlimited software upgrades at your home or office.

5. *Original* Our customer service hours are 9 a m to 5 p m

   Correct Sentence Our customer service hours are 9 a.m. to 5 p.m.

Answers to Section IX—Use the Comma Correctly

Go to **Chapter 6—Punctuate Correctly**, page 107, to review and practice using the comma correctly. You'll learn the most common and important rules for using commas correctly in writing your e-mails.

1. *Original* We have also opened corporate offices in Chicago Los Angeles and Seattle.

   Correct Sentence We have also opened corporate offices in Chicago, Los Angeles, and Seattle.

2. *Original* At any rate we can supply temporary staff if you decide to add personnel for this short-term project.

   Correct Sentence At any rate, we can supply temporary staff if you decide to add personnel for this short-term project.

3. *Original* To apply for government drought-relief funds you must complete the H39 form which establishes the dollar value of your crop loss then send the H39 to the address at the bottom of the form.

   Correct Sentence To apply for government drought-relief funds, you must complete the H39 form, which establishes the dollar value of your crop loss, then send the H39 to the address at the bottom of the form.

4. *Original* I want to return the end table I bought but I don't have the receipt anymore.

   Correct Sentence I want to return the end table I bought, but I don't have the receipt anymore.

5. *Original*   You replaced your 1997 model with the 2005 model Freda and probably saved $150 per year in operating costs.

   Correct Sentence   You replaced your 1997 model with the 2005 model**,** Freda**,** and probably saved $150 per year in operating costs.

Answers to Section X—Use the Apostrophe Correctly

Go to **Chapter 6—Punctuate Correctly**, page 110, to review and practice using the apostrophe correctly. You'll learn how to use the apostrophe in contractions and to show possession.

1. *Original*   The beneficiarys name is Patricia Arisa.

   Correct Sentence   The beneficiary**'**s name is Patricia Arisa.

2. *Original*   With Dercks enhanced service contract, you will avoid maintenance fees for almost 3 years.

   Correct Sentence   With Derck**'**s enhanced service contract, you will avoid maintenance fees for almost 3 years.

3. *Original*   I havent bought college textbooks on the Web since I began graduate school.

   Correct Sentence   I haven**'**t bought college textbooks on the Web since I began graduate school.

4. *Original*   The College Mens Intramural Sports Program is funded by alumni donations, and the College Womens Intramural Sports Program is funded by a private foundation.

   Correct Sentence   The College Men**'**s Intramural Sports Program is funded by alumni donations, and the College Women**'**s Intramural Sports Program is funded by a private foundation.

5. *Original*   When cleaning the bag attachment, its best to grasp the Weed Trimmer by its plastic handle, not the bag clip.

   Correct Sentence   When cleaning the bag attachment, it**'**s best to grasp the Weed Trimmer by its plastic handle, not the bag clip.

Go to **Chapter 6—Punctuate Correctly**, page 113, to review and practice using the semicolon correctly. You'll learn how the semicolon is different from the period or comma.

1. *Original*

   Many customers are interested in the lowest price however, that price may not buy the best product.

   Correct Sentence

   Many customers are interested in the lowest price; however, that price may not buy the best product.

2. *Original*

   You may be interested in these vacation rental properties: our two-bedroom, two-bathroom condo in Fort Lauderdale our rustic mountain cabin in the Allegheny Mountains or our three-bedroom, two-bathroom beach house on Cape Cod.

   Correct Sentence

   You may be interested in these vacation rental properties: our two-bedroom, two-bathroom condo in Fort Lauderdale; our rustic mountain cabin in the Allegheny Mountains; or our three-bedroom, two-bathroom beach house on Cape Cod.

3. *Original*

   Hosts Laura and Mitchell Brooks are a fascinating couple I can promise you'll arrive as guests and you will leave as friends.

   Correct Sentence

   Hosts Laura and Mitchell Brooks are a fascinating couple; I can promise you'll arrive as guests and you'll leave as friends.

4. *Original*

   If you're interested in earning your GED online, please contact James Hoyt, registrar Muriel Worden, student counselor and Brian Bundocks, instructor.

   Correct Sentence

   If you're interested in earning your GED online, please contact James Hoyt, registrar; Muriel Worden, student counselor; and Brian Bundocks, instructor.

5. *Original*

   We will resolve the problems you have had getting the books delivered we can send the materials by FedEx or by courier.

   Correct Sentence

   We will resolve the problems you have had getting the books delivered; we can send the materials by FedEx or by courier.

Answers to Section XII—Use the Colon Correctly

Go to **Chapter 6—Punctuate Correctly**, page 115, to review and practice using the colon correctly. You'll learn to use the colon to introduce lists and precede examples and explanations.

1. *Original*

   We are open during traditional business hours 10:00 a.m. until 7:30 p.m., Monday through Friday.

   Correct Sentence

   We are open during traditional business hours: 10:00 a.m. until 7:30 p.m., Monday through Friday.

2. *Original*

   We'll give you all the tourist information you'll need to have a great trip what sights to see, where to eat, what to do, and which local tour companies to use.

   Correct Sentence

   We'll give you all the tourist information you'll need to have a great trip: what sights to see, where to eat, what to do, and which local tour companies to use.

3. *Original*

   We have two pricing plans an annual fee of $295.00 or a monthly fee of $29.95.

   Correct Sentence

   We have two pricing plans: an annual fee of $295.00 or a monthly fee of $29.95.

4. *Original*

   Our telephone agent reports that customers are pleased with the new design of the monthly statement she received five positive phone calls about the statement on Monday morning alone.

   Correct Sentence

   Our telephone agent reports that customers are pleased with the new design of the monthly statement: she received five positive phone calls about the statement on Monday morning alone.

5. *Original*

   The following periodicals are published monthly *Burning Tree Anthology, Words Work,* and *The Special Writer.*

   Correct Sentence

   The following periodicals are published monthly: *Burning Tree Anthology, Words Work,* and *The Special Writer.*

Go to **Chapter 6—Punctuate Correctly** on page 105 to review and practice using punctuation. You'll learn to use periods, commas, apostrophes, semicolons, and colons correctly. We've provided the correct punctuation for each of the incorrect items.

I	1. Each of the products registered on our system has a $5, shipping and handling charge.
Corrected punctuation	Each of the products registered on our system has a $5 shipping and handling charge. *(no comma after $5)*
C	2. Also, if you have a problem with another purchase (and we would hope you would not), please let the store manager know.
I	3. You should go to our website: www.paulbfoods.com and click on the Products menu.
Corrected punctuation	You should go to our website, www.paulbfoods.com, and click on the Products menu.
I	4. I'm giving you two price quotes for the 16-night cruise you inquired about, Lorri; and I hope you'll contact me soon to reserve a stateroom.
Corrected punctuation	I'm giving you two price quotes for the 16-night cruise you inquired about, Lorri, and I hope you'll contact me soon to reserve a stateroom.
C	5. Home improvement loans are not subsidized by the federal government; therefore, applicants do not have to fill out the HL-619 form.
C	6. Take a steam locomotive trip in Maryland's scenic Allegheny Mountains and enjoy a bit of our region's past.
I	7. Your total of $26.84 will be charged to your credit card (please note that this charge will appear on your credit card statement from LITTLE IVAN ENTERPRISES).
Corrected punctuation	Your total of $26.84 will be charged to your credit card. **(P**lease note that this charge will appear on your credit card statement from LITTLE IVAN ENTERPRISES**.)**.
I	8. To sell an item, access it's detail page on our web site and click on the Sell button at the upper right corner of the screen.
Corrected punctuation	To sell an item, access **its** detail page on our web site and click on the Sell button at the upper right corner of the screen.
C	9. All our woodworking tools are backed by our Product Promise: if you are not entirely satisfied with a tool, return it to us at any time for an exchange or refund of its purchase price.
C	10. This message is being sent by the Confidence.com autoresponder, so no live person will see your reply.

Go to **Chapter 7—Write for Global Customers,** page 123, to review the topic and practice writing for global customers. You'll learn how to identify words or phrases that might confuse non-native English speakers, as well as how to write gender-neutral e-mail.

Did you find the idioms, gender-biased words, and other words or phrases that could confuse non-native English speakers? The parts of this e-mail that we think global customers might not understand appear in **bold** type.

To: Gsullivan@wdesw.org
From: sandy@cedarcr.com
Subject: Re: Cedar Crest online pricing

Dear Mr. Sullivan,

Thanks for **getting in touch with** Cedar Crest about prices. I'm Sandy, the **salesman in charge of** customer service. We appreciate your interest in purchasing products from us.

The products, prices, and promotions in our retail stores will sometimes differ from those offered online. **As a rule,** our retail stores don't have the capability to match online prices and **vice versa.** That capability is **in the works,** and we hope to have it **up and running soon.** Your **best bet** is to phone the retail store **ahead of time** and tell the **salesman** which products you are interested in -- woodworking tools, books, or fine craft gift items -- and give **him** the Internet prices. **He** will match those prices if the Internet prices are lower than the store prices.

Have you seen our latest **Super Stuff** bargains? We're selling everything from rocking chairs to greeting cards. You need more Super Stuff! To make sure you are **up to speed,** go to www.cedarcr.com/stuff. New offers are added **all day long, so don't be a stranger!**

We look forward to your next visit to one of our Cedar Crest stores or to www.cedarcr.com. **In the bricks-and-mortar world**, we're open from 9:30 a.m. until 9:30 p.m.

Best wishes,

Sandy and the Customer Care Team

Chapter 3
Write Clear, Strong Sentences

In this chapter, you'll learn how to

Write in the active voice
Put modifiers in the right place
Write full sentences, not run-ons or fragments
Choose strong verbs to give your writing power

A weak sentence is a lot like a junk drawer. The information is in there somewhere, but the sentence is so messy that the main point is lost in the clutter. Clear sentences are the building blocks of clear messages. Because customers use the information in your e-mail messages to decide or do something, they like concise and definite sentences. Clear sentences use as few words as possible to express the point. Clear sentences keep the subject and the verb near each other and, usually, near the beginning of the sentence.

Write in the Active Voice

Sentences can be written in active voice or passive voice. When a sentence is written in active voice, the subject of the sentence does the action of the verb. Here's an example of a sentence written in active voice: *The Service Department will send you the part you need.* The subject of this sentence is *The Service Department* and the verb is *will send.* Because *The Service Department* is doing the action of the verb *will send*, this sentence is written in active voice.

When a sentence is written in passive voice, the subject of the sentence receives the action of the verb. The subject of the sentence is passive; it is acted upon. Here is the sentence about the service department written in the passive voice: *The part you need will be sent by the Service Department.* The subject of the sentence is *The part* and the verb is *will be sent.* Because *The part* is not doing the action of the verb *will be sent*, this sentence is written in passive voice.

Don't Confuse Voice with Verb Tense

Some people confuse the passive voice with the past tense. Voice refers to the "doer" and "receiver" of the action. Past tense is a verb form that indicates that the action has already happened—it is in the past. Here's an example of a sentence with a verb in the past tense. *We mailed the package to you last Wednesday. Mailed* is the past tense of the verb *to mail.* Even though this sentence uses the past tense of the verb, it is written in the active voice. The subject, *we,* performs the action of the verb *mailed.*

Is Passive Voice Bad?

Of course not. Passive voice is not bad writing, but it does have some disadvantages for customers reading e-mail messages. Compare the two versions of the sentence below.

Active Voice   The Service Department will send you the part you need.

Passive Voice   The part you need will be sent by the Service Department.

If you were reading quickly, the way most customers read online, you would probably appreciate the active sentence because it makes clear who will do what. *The Service Department will send you the part.* To understand the passive sentence, you must read the entire sentence to know who will send you the part. Most readers find active sentences easier to understand. This is especially true when they want to know who is going to do what to answer their questions or solve their problems. The active voice highlights the "doer" in the sentence. Passive voice often sounds more formal and less friendly. Sentences written in the active voice usually use fewer words. Active voice makes your writing more concise.

How to Tell if a Sentence Is Written in Active Voice or Passive Voice

It's easy to tell if a sentence is active or passive after you identify the subject and the verb. Here are three simple steps to identifying active and passive voice:

1.   Find the subject in the sentence. Circle the subject. In the example below, the subject of the sentence is *You*.

2.   Find the verb. Underline the verb. In the example below, the verb is *may call*.

Example:

(You) <u>may call</u> the Technology Sales Group at 800-555-1390 to place an order.

3.   Ask yourself, "Is the subject of this sentence doing the action of the verb?" In our example, the subject *you* is doing the action of the verb *may call*. Therefore, the sentence is written in the active voice.

Here's how the sentence would look if it were written in the passive voice: *The Technology Sales Group may be called at 800-555-1390 to place an order.* The subject *Technology Sales Group* is not doing the action of the verb *may be called.* The "doer" of the action, omitted from the sentence but understood, is *you*.

Practice 3.1—
Change Passive Voice to Active Voice

Rewrite these passive voice sentences to make them active. For answers to **Practice 3.1**, see page 60.

1. The rack can be used by boaters to carry the boat on the top of the car.

2. A price quote will be sent to you by our customer service staff within 24 hours.

3. A problem has been caused by an upgrade to the e-mail servers you use.

4. The item number MID583 should be entered in the quick search box located in the top navigation bar.

5. The link to our free 60-day trial can be found on the left side of our home page.

Put Modifiers in the Right Place

What's a modifier, anyway? A modifier is a word or phrase that modifies, or adds meaning to, another word. Sound confusing? Actually, it's easy. An adjective can be a modifier. In this sentence, the adjective *fresh* is a modifier: *Corporate Gift Sales can send three baskets of fresh fruit to your customers.* The adjective *fresh* modifies the noun *fruit.*

An adverb can be a modifier, too. In this sentence, the adverb *slowly* is the modifier: *After receiving 100 e-mail messages in an hour, the manager slowly answered them one by one.* The adverb *slowly* modifies, or adds information about, the verb *answered.*

A phrase can be a modifier. In this sentence, the phrase *in the Owner's Manual* is the modifier: *I read the instructions in the Owner's Manual about installing a new fuse.* The phrase *in the Owner's Manual* modifies, or adds information about, where *I read the instructions about installing a new fuse.*

Problems with Modifiers Can Make Your Sentences Confusing or Funny (but Not in a Good Way)

The modifier should go near the word(s) it modifies. When the modifier appears in the wrong place, it can really cause confusion. This sentence has a modifier problem: *I send sugar cookies to my grandmother who lives in California every Christmas.* The way this sentence is written, it sounds like the writer's grandmother lives in California every Christmas. (Where does she live the rest of the year?) What the writer meant to say was that every Christmas, she sends cookies to her grandmother. By moving the modifier *every Christmas* closer to *send,* the verb it modifies, the sentence communicates what the writer meant to say. Here is the correct and clear version of the sentence: *Every Christmas, I send sugar cookies to my grandmother who lives in California.*

Watch Out for Slippery Modifiers: First, Last, Almost, Only, and Nearly

In each of these sentences, a single-word modifier is in the wrong place. Study the revision to see how moving a single word makes a sentence clear.

Modifier Problem	I read the **two** first pages of the novel before I fell asleep. (How can the novel have **two** first pages?)
Revision	I read the first **two** pages of the novel before I fell asleep.
Modifier Problem	The instructions you need can be found in the **two last chapters** of the manual. (Only one chapter of the manual can be the last chapter, right?)
Revision	The instructions you need can be found in the **last two chapters** of the manual.

Modifier Problem	The new client **almost** called all the other dealers in the Yellow Pages before reaching our company. (The client almost called, but did not pick up the phone?)
Revision	The new client called **almost** all the other dealers in the Yellow Pages before reaching our company. (The new client reached almost all the other dealers before calling our company.)
Modifier Problem	I **only** asked for overnight delivery on two of the five items. *(Only asked?* Instead of *asked, begged, pleaded, and whimpered?)*
Revision	I asked for overnight delivery on **only** two of the five items. (The other three items were delivered second class.)
Modifier Problem	Susan has **nearly** insulted every manager who has employed her. (Either Susan has insulted her manager or she hasn't. How can a manager be nearly insulted?)
Revision	Susan has insulted **nearly** every manager who has employed her.

Study These Modifier Revisions

All the sentences in this table have modifier problems. Read the original sentence, then read the solution to the problem. Finally, read the revised sentence.

Sentence with Modifier Problem	Solution	Revised Sentence
I ordered the "How to Complete a Job Application" brochure for our community center in English, Vietnamese, and Spanish.	Move the phrase in *English, Vietnamese,* and *Spanish* near *brochure*, the noun it modifies.	I ordered the "How to Complete a Job Application" brochure in English, Vietnamese, and Spanish for our community center.
I would like to return a video I have opened and played *because I am very disappointed in it.*	Move the clause *because I am very disappointed in it* nearer the word it modifies: *return.*	Because I am very disappointed in it, I would like to return a video I have opened and played.
Customers who buy online regularly complain about sites that are unequipped to process orders.	Do the customers buy *regularly* or do they complain *regularly*? Move the word *regularly* to clarify the meaning.	Customers who regularly buy online complain about sites that are unequipped to process orders. —or— Customers who buy online complain regularly about sites that are unequipped to process orders.
I tried to log on to your Web-based Help Center about returning the software I bought from you while I was on hold on the telephone.	Move the clause *while I was on hold on the telephone* to the beginning of the sentence to avoid confusion. Did the customer mean he bought the software *while* on hold? No.	While I was on hold on the telephone, I tried to log on to your Web-based Help Center to find out about returning the software I bought from you.

Practice 3.2—
Move Modifiers to Make Sentences Clearer

Revise these sentences to remove confusion caused by problem modifiers. In some sentences you'll move only one word. In other sentences you'll move a phrase or a clause. For answers to **Practice 3.2**, see page 60.

1. If you wish to search only one of the categories, make sure it is the one selected only at the top of the search form.

2. The first available specialist will be contacting you by e-mail or telephone within one business day to quickly provide a solution to your request.

3. Some customer service agents nearly spend all their workday on the telephone.

4. Because of the manufacturer's restrictions, we are only allowed to have this item active until 2:00 a.m. EST.

5. In addition to the excellent discounts offered by Cruiseliner.com, I've personally researched and reviewed your quote request to ensure that you receive the cruise line's most favorable rate.

6. In order to better serve you, please access our online billing center at http://support.iwebland.com.

7. The Business Information Bureau nearly has 1,000 listings for local entrepreneurs.

8. My best customer asked me why our company's pricing is better than our competition's pricing last week.

9. While attending an approved public university, the federal government pays the interest on your daughter's school loan.

10. Too small, the wrong color, or no longer needed, we are willing to refund the full price of the product if you return the item unused, in its original packaging.

Write Full Sentences (Not Fragments or Run-Ons)

Fragments and run-ons occur when you punctuate a group of words as if they are a complete sentence, but they're not. A complete sentence has at least one independent clause (a group of words that contains a subject and a verb and makes sense by itself). A fragment is just a part of a sentence, but it's punctuated with a period at the end, making it look like a full sentence. A run-on is more than one sentence punctuated as if it were one sentence. Run-ons are usually two or more sentences patched together with commas.

Some people think that because e-mail is more casual than a print letter, it's not important to write full sentences. That's just wrong. Full sentences make your writing easier to understand because they express complete ideas.

Fragments Are Incomplete Sentences

Here's an example of a fragment: *To get better acquainted with Invest Now magazine.* This fragment does not make sense by itself. A fragment is just a group of words—a phrase or a dependent clause—but not a full sentence. When you put a period at the end of a fragment, it may look like a sentence, but it's still a fragment.

How to Fix a Fragment

Here are two ways to make a fragment into a complete sentence:

1.   Join the fragment to the sentence that comes before it or after it.

Fragment Example   While we would prefer to do an exchange.

Correct Sentence   While we would prefer to do an exchange, we are willing to refund the full price of the product if the item is returned in its original packing.

2.   Rewrite the fragment and make it a complete sentence.

Fragment Example   In order to assist you.

Correct Sentence   To assist you, we will look up the tracking number you've given us.

Revise these fragments to make them full sentences. You may add information or rewrite the sentences as necessary. For answers to **Practice 3.3**, see page 61.

1. Thanking you for shopping at SilverCatalog.com.

2. Or, if the credit card receipt should be sent to someone else.

3. If there hasn't been any activity on your account within the past 6 months.

4. Broken link at the Web site.

5. Because we have completed your request.

6. Enough power to run this program.

7. After Thanksgiving to give you good results through the Christmas holiday.

8. For immediate assistance.

9. Issues pertaining to ordering from our online store.

10. Sold approximately 1,000 units nationwide.

Run-Ons Are Two or More Sentences Linked by Incorrect Punctuation

Here's an example of a run-on: *We have your payment, it was posted on February 22, 2005.* When you hook two sentences (independent clauses) together with a comma, that's called a comma splice. Don't choose a comma to join two sentences.

How to Fix a Run-On

You can fix a run-on in several different ways.

1. Divide the run-on into two or more complete sentences. Use a period at the end of each sentence.

Run-On Example	I am glad you found us, please share this information with others you know who would appreciate this unique opportunity.
Correct Sentence	I am glad you found us. Please share this information with others you know who would appreciate this unique opportunity.

2. Turn the run-on sentence into a compound sentence. You can do this in three different ways:

    • Add a comma and a coordinating conjunction such as *and, or, nor, but, yet, so, for.*

Run-On Example	You can send me a short text message any time, I will receive it on my pager.
Correct Sentence	You can send me a short text message any time, and I will receive it on my pager.

    • Use a semicolon to separate the two independent clauses.

Run-On Example	I'm giving you two quotes on ocean-view staterooms on the 16-night Sunset Ocean cruise you requested, one stateroom has a porthole and the other has a picture window.
Correct Sentence	I'm giving you two quotes on ocean-view staterooms on the 16-night Sunset Ocean cruise you requested; one stateroom has a porthole and the other has a picture window.

    • Add a semicolon and an adverb (such as *however* or *therefore*) followed by a comma.

Run-On Example	You may submit your request online, if you need a different airport drop-off location or special equipment, please call us at 800–CAR–CALL.
Correct Sentence	You may submit your request online; however, if you need a different airport drop-off location or special equipment, please call us at 800–CAR–CALL.

Revise these run-on sentences to make them into full sentences. For answers to **Practice 3.4**, see page 62.

1. Unfortunately, we do not have an e-mail support area for our credit card accounts, we request that you contact our Card Products Division at 800–555–9131.

2. Representatives are available 24 hours a day, seven days a week, we sincerely apologize for any inconvenience this may have caused.

3. Thank you for choosing a Marksman vacuum cleaner, because I do not know your model number, I don't know the exact nature of your plug/power cord problem.

4. It would be best if you took your ink-jet printer to an authorized dealer, perhaps the one you purchased it from can determine if there is a problem that can be corrected.

5. This is in response to your e-mail concerning FireFly smoke detectors, the FireFly photoelectric model 480 does not have battery back-up but should be vacuumed regularly to remove dust, dirt, and insects that can accumulate in the back of the detector.

6. Shut off the circuit breaker that provides electricity to that unit, place a screw-driver under the lip of the plug, and twist, this will move the plug off the pins of the detector.

7. I just tested your e-mail account and it is fine, an upgrade to the e-mail servers caused a problem.

8. Please be patient as it may take 24 to 48 hours for some owners to respond, it will take more time if they are traveling.

9. Thank you for shopping at SuperToy, we sincerely appreciate your business and look forward to seeing you online again soon!

10. From the start page, you can continue an existing application, if your application has been submitted, you can add additional employers to your list.

11. We've received your request for help, we will be in touch with you within the next 24 hours.

Choose Strong Verbs to Give Your Writing Power

Strong verbs give your writing muscle; they make your sentences powerful and clear. Weak or bland verbs make your writing less forceful. You can often replace forms of the verb *to be*, including *am, is, are, was, were, be, being,* and *been* with more precise verbs for clearer, more powerful writing.

Weak Verb   The search engine **is set up** to automatically search both program site descriptions and program course descriptions.

Strong Verb   The search engine automatically **searches** both program site descriptions and program course descriptions.

The "There Is/It Is" Problem

You can also give your sentences power by removing empty words such as *it is*, *there is*, and *there are*. These words take up the important subject and verb slots in your sentence. Using *it* or *there* as the subject and *is* or *are* as the verb weakens your sentence. Replace *it is, there is,* and *there are* constructions with stronger beginnings or rearrange the sentence to feature more interesting words.

Weak Verb   **If there is** anything else that I can do for you, please don't hesitate to notify me.

Strong Verb   If **I can do** anything else for you, please don't hesitate to notify me.

Weak Verb   **There is** a six-item minimum per fabric type when ordering our product with your logo applied to it.

Strong Verb   **We set** a six-item minimum per fabric type when you order our product with your logo applied to it.

"Smothered" Verbs Are Verbs "Trapped" in Noun Form

Sometimes writers take perfectly good verbs and turn them into nouns, thus robbing them of their power in sentences. These verbs-turned-into-nouns are sometimes called "smothered" verbs. For example, think of the verb *suggest* and its noun form *suggestion*. Here's a sentence using the verb *suggest*: *We suggest the Model 341Z camera, a product that will fit your needs.* Now that's a good, clear sentence with the strong verb *suggest*. But here's what happens when we use the noun form *suggestion*: *Our suggestion for a product that will fit your needs is the Model 341Z camera.* In this sentence, *suggestion* is a smothered verb. As you can see, we've had to choose *is*, a weak verb, to make the sentence complete.

How can you recognize verbs in noun form? One way is to look for *–ment*, *–ence*, or *–tion* endings in the noun form. Here's an example: *We will give you information about new releases of our graphic design software.* The word *information* is a smothered verb; *information* is the noun form of the verb *inform*. Here's the sentence using the verb *inform*: *We will inform you monthly about new releases of our graphic design software.* Now that's a clear sentence!

Practice 3.5—
Replace Weak Verbs with Strong Verbs

Underline the verb in each of these sentences. Then, rewrite the sentence to replace the weak or smothered verb with a powerful verb. For answers to **Practice 3.5**, see page 63.

1. Our webmaster will make the necessary arrangements to remove you from our mailing list, if you so desire.

2. It is our policy to provide you with an estimate within 24 hours after we receive your request.

3. Please make contact with us by phone if you want more help.

4. It is best to clean the filter using the detergent supplied by the manufacturer.

5. We have made the correction to your address, as you requested.

6. At our web site, you can make a selection of one of our several delivery options.

7. There are so many different types of amplifiers available for guitar players to buy.

8. You can do your loan application online or in person at any one of our branch offices.

9. Our bank gives an interest rate reduction for any person who has an existing car loan with us.

10. The Golden Skies Resort has worked on preservation of several exotic plants growing on our property.

Answers to Practice 3.1—Change Passive Voice to Active Voice

We have revised these sentences to put them in active voice.

1. Boaters can use the rack to carry the boat on the top of the car.

2. Our customer service staff will send you a price quote within 24 hours.

3. An upgrade to the e-mail servers you use has caused an unforeseen problem.

4. You should enter the item number MID583 in the quick search box located in the top navigation bar.

5. You can find the link to our free 60-day trial on the left side of our home page.

Answers to Practice 3.2—Move Modifiers to Make Sentences Clearer

We have revised these sentences to remove confusion caused by problem modifiers. The words in **bold** type are the modifiers we moved. In some cases, we revised other words in the sentence to make the sentence clearer.

1. If you wish to search only one of the categories, make sure it is the **only** one selected at the top of the search form.

2. **Within one business day**, the first available specialist will be contacting you by e-mail or telephone to quickly provide a solution to your request.

3. Some customer service agents spend **nearly** all their workday on the telephone.

4. Because of the manufacturer's restrictions, we are allowed to have this item active **only** until 2 a.m. EST.

5. I've personally researched and reviewed your quote request to ensure that you receive Cruiseliner.com's most favorable rate **in addition to the excellent discounts.**

6. Please access our online billing center at www.support.iwebland.com **so we may better serve you.**

7. The Business Information Bureau has **nearly** 1,000 listings for local entrepreneurs.

8. **Last week** my best customer asked me why our company's pricing is better than our competition's pricing.

9.   The federal government pays the interest on your daughter's school loan **while she's attending an approved public university.**

10.   We are willing to refund the full price of the product **(too small, the wrong color, or no longer needed)** if you return the item unused, in its original packaging.

Answers to Practice 3.3—Change Fragments into Full Sentences

We have revised these fragments to make them full sentences. The words in **bold** type are the ones we changed or added to make the fragment a full sentence.

1.   **Thank** you for shopping at SilverCatalog.com.

2.   **Please tell us** if the credit card receipt should be sent to someone else.

3.   If there hasn't been any activity on your account within the past 6 months, **it will be closed.**

4.   **The broken link at the Web site has been fixed.**

5.   We have completed your request.

                          —or—

      Because we have completed your request, we hope you will order from us again soon.

6.   **Your machine should have** enough power to run this program.

7.   **We suggest you buy the live tree** after Thanksgiving to give you good results through the Christmas holiday.

8.   For immediate assistance, **please call 800–555–4141.**

9.   For issues pertaining to ordering from our online store, **please e-mail us at help@online.com.**

10.   **We have** sold approximately 1,000 units nationwide.

Answers to Practice 3.4—Change Run-ons into Full Sentences

We've revised these run-on sentences to make them full sentences. The words and punctuation in **bold** type show our revisions. In most cases, there is more than one correct way to change a run-on sentence into a full sentence, so your revisions may be different from these.

1. Unfortunately, we do not have an e-mail support area for our credit card accounts; **therefore**, we request that you contact our Card Products Division at 800–555–9131.

2. Representatives are available 24 hours a day, seven days a week. **We** sincerely apologize for any inconvenience this may have caused.

3. Thank you for choosing a Marksman vacuum cleaner; **however, because I don't know your model number,** I don't know the exact nature of your plug/power cord problem.

4. It would be best if you took your ink-jet printer to an authorized dealer. **Perhaps** the one you purchased it from can determine if there is a problem that can be corrected.

5. This is in response to your e-mail concerning FireFly smoke detectors. **The** FireFly photoelectric model 480 does not have battery back-up but should be vacuumed regularly to remove dust, dirt, and insects that can accumulate in the back of the detector.

6. Shut off the circuit breaker that provides electricity to that unit, place a screwdriver under the lip of the plug, and twist. **This** will move the plug off the pins of the detector.

7. I just tested your e-mail account and it is fine**;** an upgrade to the e-mail servers caused an unforeseen problem.

8. Please be patient as it may take 24 to 48 hours for some owners to respond. **It** will take more time if they are traveling.

9. Thank you for shopping at SuperToy. **We** sincerely appreciate your business and look forward to seeing you online again soon!

10. From the start page, you can continue an existing application. **If** your application has been submitted, you can add additional employers to your list.

11. We've received your request for help. **We** will be in touch with you within the next 24 hours.

We've revised these sentences, replacing weak verbs with strong ones. The words in **bold** type show our revisions. In most cases, there is more than one correct way to correct the weak verb problem, so your revisions may be different from these.

1.   Our webmaster will **arrange** to remove you from our mailing list, if you so desire.

—or—

Our webmaster **will remove** you from our mailing list, if you so desire.

2.   Our policy states that we **will provide** you with an estimate within 24 hours after we receive your request.

3.   Please **call us** if you want more help.

4.   To best clean the filter, **use** the detergent supplied by the manufacturer.

5.   **We've corrected** your address in our system, as you requested.

6.   At our Web site, you can **select** one of our several delivery options.

7.   Guitar players can **buy one** of many different types of available amplifiers.

8.   You can **apply for** your loan online or in person at any one of our branch offices.

9.   Our bank **reduces the** interest rate for any person who has an existing car loan with us.

10.   The Golden Skies Resort has **preserved** several exotic plants growing on our property.

Chapter 4
Write with a Polite, Positive, and Personal Tone

In this chapter, you'll learn how

Words affect tone
Personalizing your e-mail makes customers feel valued
Plain, simple language contributes to a polite, positive, and personal tone

Tone—or how the words you choose show your attitude toward your customer—is particularly important in customer service e-mail. In a phone call, a customer can hear your cheerful voice. In a formal letter, your corporate letterhead or gold-embossed stationery gives you credibility. With e-mail, you have only words with which to make an impression on a customer.

Here is an e-mail response a customer received from Universe Communications. How do you think the tone of this e-mail affects the customer's opinion of the company?

Dear Valued Customer,

We have received your e-mail and will process your request within two business days during our regular business hours. If we need additional information or need to contact you about our actions we will respond with a second e-mail.

If you are contacting us with a technical concern, please allow more processing time as we may need to contact our technical staff for resolution.

If you do not hear from us, it's because we have completed your request.

Although the e-mail refers to a "Valued Customer," the response makes the customer feel anything but valued. The tone of the message—its attitude—communicates, "You are not important, your query is an inconvenience, and we will respond when it suits us!"

In responding to customer service e-mail, it's important to solve your customer's problems. But it is equally important to create goodwill by showing customers that you value them. A positive tone in your e-mail messages can make your customers feel valued.

These four responses to a customer, explaining why his cable service was disconnected, contain the same information, but the tone is noticeably different depending on the words.

Angry Tone   Because you did not pay your long-overdue bill and have not responded to our repeated phone calls, we have cut off your service.

Inflated Tone   Pursuant to our service agreement, please be advised that after an account is in arrears in excess of 90 days, Seaside Cable has the right to terminate service.

Polite Tone   Our policy is to discontinue service when a payment is more than 90 days overdue.

Apologetic Tone   We're sorry that we disconnected your service. It's our policy to do so when an account is more than 90 days overdue.

As a writer, you control the tone of your e-mail by the words you choose. Circle the words or phrases that create the tone of each of the four messages above. Then compare the circled words in the angry and inflated messages with the circled words in the apologetic and polite messages.

When responding to an angry customer's e-mail, you may be tempted to match the customer's tone. Don't! Before sending your response, make sure it does not contain words or phrases that show anger or annoyance.

Practice 4.1—
Revise an Angry E-Mail to Make It Polite and Positive

A customer wrote an angry letter to the Springer Company. Then, the customer service agent responded with an angry tone. First, circle the words or phrases that create the angry tone. Then, revise or rewrite the agent's reply to make the tone polite and positive. When you've completed your revision, look at page 84 to see how we revised the e-mail.

Customer E-Mail

> To: customer_service@springer.com
> From: jm@mailman.com
> Subject: I WANT TO RETURN SOMETHING!
>
> Springer Company!!
>
> I spent an hour trying to REMOVE an item (the purple sweater, size small) from my shopping cart. I finally gave up. At that point, I wanted to cancel the whole darn order, but I didn't have time to run to the store to buy the other items -- that's why I was shopping online.
>
> So, I ordered and paid for the sweater that I didn't want. Now I want to return it. The instructions for returns are about as clear as the instructions for deleting items from my cart (that is, NONEXISTENT).
>
> I do not want the sweater. Can you please tell me how to return it?
>
> Jim McAllister

To: jm@mailman.com
From: customer_service@springer.com
Subject: HOW TO RETURN AN ITEM

Mr. McAllister:

It is not hard to REMOVE an item from your shopping cart. Simply click on "Remove an item." Then give the item number for the item you want to delete. Most customers do not have trouble with this.

It is not hard to return an item, either. You should be able to follow the simple instructions under RETURNS. But since you cannot find or follow these simple instructions, I will tell you how to return an item.

1. On the home page menu, click on "Returns."

2. Fill out the RETURN form that came with your order. It is very clear and simple. Tell us WHY you are returning the item, and FILL OUT your name and address.

3. Send the item back in its original packing. Insure the item, and KEEP A RECORD of your return receipt. Upon receipt of the return, we will credit your account.

I hope that this is simple enough for you to understand.

Thank you for your e-mail. Please let me know if I can provide additional assistance.

Arlene Springer
Customer Service, Springer Company

Practice 4.1—
Your Revision to the Angry E-Mail Response from the Springer Company

Customers don't like to read e-mails that seem to be written by a computer. They want to hear from a person. But that's not the only reason to personalize your response to your customer. You want to build a relationship with your customer, and a personalized response to an e-mail query helps to do that.

You're probably thinking that personalizing a response takes a lot of time—time you don't have. But once you get in the habit of "thinking personal," you'll begin to do it automatically.

Greet Your Customer by Name

It's easy to personalize your e-mail by using the customer's name instead of a generic greeting such as *Dear Customer* or no greeting at all.

Your company policy may specify what greeting to use in your customer service e-mail: first name, last name, or both. Your relationship with the customer, your company's image, or the contents of the e-mail may determine whether you use the more formal greeting, *Dear Roger Anderson,* or an informal greeting such as *Hi, Roger!*

Use the E-Mail Opening to Set the Tone

As a busy agent, your inclination is to get right to the point. Your job is to answer the question and go on to the next customer's e-mail.

But remember, the tone of your e-mail is as important as the content. The opening sets the tone for your e-mail. Take an extra minute to craft the opening. Here are three techniques for setting a personal tone with the opening.

1. **Restate the customer's question.**

   Thank you for your e-mail asking how to purchase a gift certificate.

2. **Personalize the opening by using what you know about the customer.**

   We are sorry that you canceled your subscription to "EcoBusiness." We are always concerned when a subscriber is unhappy with our newsletter.

3. **Personalize the e-mail by introducing yourself.**

   This is Julie Eaton at Cruise100. I've personally researched and reviewed your quote request to ensure that you receive the cruise line's most favorable rate.

This e-mail comes from a longtime customer to Daybook, a company that sells day planners.

> *I've been using Daybook products for years. That's why I'm extremely upset that you spelled my name wrong on my personal memo pads. I'm returning the memo pads. Can you print them correctly? The name on the pads should be Thomas P. Eagan, NOT Thomas P. Eager.*

Here is the response that the Daybook agent sent Mr. Eagan.

> *We have reprinted the memo pads with the correct spelling of your name. We shipped the new pads today by overnight express.*

This response explains how the company has corrected the problem with Mr. Eagan's memo pads. The action is appropriate, and the response answers Mr. Eagan's question. But the tone of the message is impersonal. While it resolves Mr. Eagan's problem, it might not satisfy a disgruntled customer who wants to know that the company values his business.

This opening, in **bold** type, personalizes the e-mail and makes Mr. Eagan feel valued.

> **As a longtime customer, you're our most valued client. So we are especially sorry to have misspelled your name on your personal memo sheets.**
>
> *We have reprinted the memo pads with the correct spelling of your name. We shipped the new pads today by overnight express.*

Use the E-Mail Closing to Reinforce the Tone

You've personalized the message opening and answered the customer's question. So don't end the e-mail with a standard, impersonal closing such as *If we may be of further assistance, please contact us.*

Using this closing with your personalized e-mail is like ending a romantic dinner with stale cake. The dessert destroys the mood. And as the last course, it's the taste that lingers. Your e-mail closing will similarly linger in your customer's mind. Don't let your closing undercut the friendly, personal tone of your e-mail.

Your closing should echo the tone of your e-mail and reinforce your main point or the action you'll take. Below, in **bold** type, is a good example of a personalized closing for the e-mail to Mr. Eagan.

As a longtime customer, you're our most valued customer. So we are especially sorry to have misspelled your name on your personal memo sheets.

We have reprinted the memo pads with the correct spelling of your name. We shipped the new pads today by overnight express.

We hope that these new pads meet with your approval. We will take extra care to fill your future orders quickly and correctly.

By using a personal opening and closing in the e-mail, the agent has done more than just respond to the customer's query. The tone of the e-mail reinforces the customer's value to the company.

Sign Your Response with a Name, Not a Department

Your signature line also personalizes the response. Ending your e-mail with the name of a person, instead of just your company's name or "Customer Service Department," lets the customer know that a caring person—not an impersonal automated system—is responding.

Practice 4.2—
Write a Personalized Greeting, Opening, and Closing

A customer has e-mailed Christmas All Year asking about a tabletop Christmas tree. The agent's response is incomplete. We've provided the body of a response to customer Karen Becker. You get to be the Christmas All Year customer service agent. Please complete the e-mail response by adding a personal greeting, opening, closing, and signature. For our version of a complete response to **Practice 4.2**, see page 85.

Customer E-Mail

To:	customerservice@ChristmasAllYear.com
From:	Karen_Becker@chs.com
Subject:	Christmas Tree

I love your Christmas catalog. I have a couple of questions about the tabletop tree on p.153 of your catalog.

Can it be shipped to the 92039 zip code in California?

How long can I expect the tabletop tree to last?

Thanks.

Karen Becker

To: Karen_Becker@chs.com
From: customerservice@ChristmasAllYear.com
Subject: Re: Christmas Tree

Write a greeting:

_____

_____

Write an opening:

_____

_____

The body:

At this time there is no restriction for shipping the balsam tabletop tree to the California zip code 92039. Unfortunately, the California Department of Agriculture does have the right to ban agricultural imports on short notice. Although I believe you will have no problem, I cannot guarantee delivery. If the agriculture department bans the tree after you've ordered it, we will refund your purchase price (with shipping).

The tree should last for a few weeks. It is a live balsam product that needs to be watered occasionally. The humidity in the air will affect how long the tree lasts. We have sold our balsam products for many years and find that delivering the balsam just before Christmas will give you good results through the Christmas holiday.

Write a closing:

_____

_____

Write a signature:

_____

_____

Use Pronouns to Give Your E-Mail a Personal Tone

To make your e-mail personal, address your customer directly. Use the pronoun *you*. Use the pronouns *I, we, our,* and *us* when referring to yourself or your organization.

Write	**You** need to submit **your** doctor's report so that **we** may reimburse you.
Don't Write	A doctor's report must be submitted in order to receive reimbursement.
Write	All of **our** rooms are lovely, but **you** will find the Executive Suite particularly luxurious.
Don't Write	All rooms are lovely, but the Executive Suite is particularly luxurious.

Practice 4.3—
Revise Using Personal Pronouns to Improve Tone

Revise or rewrite these sentences from customer service e-mails by using personal pronouns. For answers to **Practice 4.3**, see page 86.

1. The daybed may be returned within 30 days of receipt for a full refund of merchandise and shipping charges.

2. Gift certificates cannot be ordered by mail, but they can be ordered by telephone or at the Web site.

3. There is no time limit for using the merchandise credit.

4. At this time, this item is available only through the catalog department.

5. Because of additional security measures, curbside check-in is no longer available.

Do your e-mails sound like they were written by the same person who writes tax forms? Do they include overused expressions and inflated words? They shouldn't. Unless you are a tax collector, don't sound like one. Your e-mails should be written in plain, easy-to-understand language.

You may be choosing words and phrases that are overused or inflated because you think they make you sound more educated or because you think they are more formal or even better English. But inflated language often makes something simple sound complex or threatening. When choosing words to use in customer service e-mail, ask yourself, "Have I written as simply and clearly as I can?"

These examples show how to simplify sentences that use inflated language so your customers won't be confused or offended by your tone.

Inflated language	We acknowledge receipt of your inquiry about your application. You must complete and return this application by October 15. Failure to do so will result in your application being rejected.
Plain language	Thanks for your e-mail asking about your application. Please complete and return this application by the October 15 deadline. We can't consider applications submitted after that date.
Inflated language	Please be advised that we cannot give you credit for the laptop computer that you returned due to the fact that it has been submerged in water, in violation of our warranty agreement.
Plain language	We are sorry we can't give you credit for the laptop computer you returned to us. We found the damage to it was caused by water. Our warranty does not cover water damage.
Inflated language	As per your request, I am enclosing herewith a copy of the software license agreement. Pursuant to our conversation, the agreement will go into effect upon receipt of said agreement, properly signed.
Plain language	As you requested, I'm sending you a copy of the software license agreement. The license period will begin once we receive the signed agreement.

Practice 4.4—
Replace These Inflated Expressions with Plain Language

Here's a list of wordy, overused, and inflated expressions that frequently appear in customer service e-mails. Write plain-language substitutes for these inflated expressions. For answers to **Practice 4.4**, see page 87.

Write Plain Language Substitutes for Inflated Expressions

Inflated Language	Plain Language
after the completion of	
as per your request	
at the present time as this point in time	
available options	
due to the fact that	
failure to do so if you fail to you failed to	
for the most part	
for the purpose of	
herewith	
in lieu of	
in the event that	
in violation of	
on or before December 15	
on the basis of	
our records indicate	
please be advised	
pursuant to our conversation	
reach a decision	
unresolved problem	
we acknowledge receipt of	
we regret to inform you	
with regard to with reference to	
your complaint	

Avoid "Insider's Language"

Insider's language, or jargon, includes those words or phrases that you understand and use at work all the time, but that outsiders—like your customers—may not know. The customer service industry has its own insider's language. For example, while you know that *ASA* stands for average speed of answer, *IPS* means items per sale, and *net reps* are call-center representatives who handle e-mail inquiries, your customers probably don't know these terms.

The products or services your company offers have probably generated their own insider's language. For example, if you sell computers, words like *docking station* or *CD-RW drive* may be part of your everyday vocabulary, but they may be unknown terms to your customers.

What insider words, phrases, or abbreviations do you use frequently that might confuse your customers? List them in the chart below, along with a simpler, more familiar phrase or explanation that you can use instead.

Insider's Language	Simple Substitute

Practice 4.5—
Revise Using Plain Language

Here's an e-mail from a customer inquiring about paying for a college transcript by check, followed by the agent's response. The customer's pleasant query receives an inflated response from the agent, Amelia. Circle the words or phrases in the agent's response that create the inflated tone. Then revise the response by substituting plain language for inflated language. We've provided space in the e-mail to write your revisions. Compare your revisions with ours on page 88.

Customer E-Mail

To:	Registrar@umd.edu
From:	John@umd.edu
Subject:	Transcript

I'm a 1990 graduate and I used the online service to request a transcript to be sent to Georgetown University, since I'm applying to graduate school. I do not have a credit card to pay the $15 transcript fee. Can I pay by check? If the answer is yes, what is the process I need to go through? I'm looking forward to a quick response.

John

Agent Response

To: John@umd.edu
From: Registrar@umd.edu
Subject: Re:Transcript

Dear John,

We acknowledge receipt of your inquiry with regard to paying for a

transcript by check. Please be advised that if you do not have a credit

card, you cannot request a transcript using our online service. You can

pay by check, but you must then request and complete a paper transcript

request form. Please call 800-555-8787 and ask customer service to mail

you the form. You must include a check (or money order) for the full

amount due when you send back your completed request form. Credit

card payment results in faster processing. In the event that you fail to

enclose payment, we cannot process your request.

Amelia
Registrar's Office, University of Morganwood

Practice 4.6—
Write with a Polite, Positive, and Personal Tone

Practice everything you've learned about tone by writing a response to this customer's e-mail. Use the *Checklist: Write with a Polite, Positive, and Personal Tone,* below, to make sure you've used a variety of techniques to create a polite, positive, and personal tone. Show your completed e-mail to a colleague or supervisor and ask for feedback. Does your reader find the tone polite, positive, and personal?

Customer E-Mail

To:	customerservice@magazinecenter.com
From:	Penelope.Quarles@webworld.com
Subject:	Problems with Invoice

I have received yet ANOTHER invoice. This makes the third invoice I've received that says I need to pay SINCE I made my payment. There must be a MAJOR problem in your invoicing/payments processing. Would you PLEASE make sure that I don't receive another invoice?

The thing that's really ironic is that I've received many invoices and NO magazine. Can you fix this?

Penelope Quarles

Checklist: Write with a Polite, Positive, and Personal Tone

___ Use the customer's name in the greeting.

___ Set the tone with a personalized opening.

___ Use personal pronouns (*I, we, our, you, your*).

___ Avoid angry words or phrases.

___ Avoid inflated words or phrases.

___ Avoid insider's language.

___ Reinforce the tone with a personal closing.

Practice 4.6—
Your Polite, Positive, and Personal Response

Here's how we revised agent Arlene Springer's response to Jim McAllister. We made the tone polite and positive. How does the tone of your revision compare with ours?

To: jm@mailman.com
From: customer service@springer.com
Subject: How to return an item

Dear Mr. McAllister,

We're sorry that you had trouble using our shopping cart. We are working hard to make it user friendly. I've sent a copy of your e-mail to our Web team members and asked them to review the instructions for removing and returning items.

Removing an item from our shopping cart should be easy. Click on "Remove an item." Then give the item number for the item you want to delete. The shopping cart should then show that this item has been removed from your cart.

Here's how to return the purple sweater or any other item.

On the home page menu, click on "Returns." Then follow these two steps:

1. Fill out the RETURN form that came with your order. Be sure to complete the entire form. Make sure that you tell us why you are returning the item and that you provide your name and complete address.

2. Send the item back in its original packing. Insure the item and keep a record of your return receipt. We will credit your account when we receive the return.

We appreciate your business and hope that your next order with us will be easier to complete. Please let me know if I can provide additional assistance.

Arlene Springer
Customer Service, Springer Company

Here's how we completed the e-mail response to Karen Becker by adding a personal greeting, opening, closing, and signature.

To: Karen Becker@chs.com
From: customerservice@ChristmasAllYear.com
Subject: Re: Christmas Tree

Write a greeting:
Dear Karen,

Write an opening:
We're glad to hear how much you like our Christmas catalog. We're happy to answer your questions about our tabletop tree.

The body:
At this time there is no restriction for shipping the balsam tabletop tree to the California zip code 92039. Unfortunately, the California Department of Agriculture does have the right to ban agricultural imports on short notice. Although I believe you will have no problem, I cannot guarantee delivery. If the agriculture department bans the tree after you've ordered it, we will refund your purchase price (with shipping).

The tree should last for a few weeks. It is a live balsam product that needs to be watered occasionally. The humidity in the air will affect how long the tree lasts. We have sold our balsam products for many years and find that delivering the balsam just before Christmas will give you good results through the Christmas holiday.

Write a closing:
We know that you will enjoy the tabletop tree this Christmas. Please let me know if you have any additional questions about the tree or any of our Christmas catalog items.

Write a signature:
Sincerely,

Shannon Lester
Customer Service Agent
ChristmasAllYear.com

Answers to Practice 4.3—Revise Using Personal Pronouns

We've revised these sentences from customer service e-mails by using personal pronouns where appropriate. Because there is more than one way to revise these sentences, your revisions may be different.

1. You may return the daybed within 30 days of receipt for a full refund of merchandise and shipping charges.

2. You cannot order gift certificates by mail, but you can order them by telephone or on our Web site.

3. We do not set a time limit for using the merchandise credit.

4. You can purchase this item through our catalog department only.

5. Because of additional security measures, you can no longer use curbside check-in.

Answers to Practice 4.4—
Replace These Inflated Expressions with Plain Language

This list provides good plain-language substitutes for wordy, overused, or inflated phrases. You may have found other simple substitutes for the inflated expressions.

Plain Language Substitutes for Inflated Expressions

Inflated Language	Plain Language
after the completion of	after completing
as per your request	as you requested
at the present time as this point in time	now
available options	options
due to the fact that	because
failure to do so if you fail to you failed to	if you do not you did not
for the most part	mostly
for the purpose of	for
herewith	delete this word entirely, no substitution necessary
in lieu of	instead of
in the event that	if
in violation of	violates
on or before December 15	by December 15
on the basis of	based on
our records indicate	our records show
please be advised	delete phrase entirely, no substitution necessary
pursuant to our conversation	as we discussed
reach a decision	decide
unresolved problem	problem
we acknowledge receipt of	we received
we regret to inform you	we're sorry
with regard to with reference to	about
your complaint	your problem

The words or expressions in **bold** type contribute to the e-mail's inflated tone. We've written plain language substitutes above the inflated language.

To: John@umd.edu
From: Registrar
Subject: Re: Transcript

Dear John,

received *about*
We **acknowledge receipt of** your inquiry **with regard to** paying

for a transcript by check. If you do not have a credit card, you

cannot request a transcript using our online service. You can pay by

check, but you must then request and complete a paper transcript request

form. Please call 800-555-8787 and ask customer service to mail you the

Please
form. **You must** include a check (or money order) for the full

amount when you send back your completed request form. Credit card

If you do not
payment results in faster processing. **In the event that you fail to**

enclose payment, we cannot process your request.

Amelia
Registrar's Office, University of Morganwood

Chapter 5
Select the Correct Word and Spell It Right

In this chapter, you'll learn

Why spelling matters
How to become a better speller
How to distinguish between confusing sound-alike and look-alike words

Does spelling matter? Some agents say, "It's only e-mail; it's not important. It takes too long to spell check each e-mail." But an e-mail with misspellings makes a poor impression: you are sloppy; you are not professional. Your company does not care about its customers.

Spelling Does Matter!

What would you think if you received this e-mail response to a message inquiring about a product guarantee?

Our product quarantee is "Gauranteed Period."

Not only is *guaranteed* misspelled, but it is misspelled two different ways! If you were the customer who received that e-mail, the sloppy spelling might make you worry about the guarantee, or whether your purchase would be shipped on time, or if your credit card would be billed correctly. Finally, you might see whether you could purchase this product somewhere else—with a more reliable "guarantee."

Spell-check programs are a great help to many poor spellers, bad typists, and busy agents who often don't take the time to proofread their e-mails before sending them. Spell-check programs flag many misspelled words. Some automatically correct commonly misspelled words.

But poor spellers often find that spell-check is only a partial solution. Spell-check may not recognize your misspelling, so it offers no correct choices. Or it could display more than one likely candidate for the correctly spelled word. Sometimes you can find the correct spelling by leafing through the dictionary. But if you truly have no idea of how to spell a word, you could spend a long time skimming dictionary pages looking for the correct spelling.

Compile Your Own Spelling List

One way to become a better speller is to compile your own list of words you frequently misspell. List them in this chart. Once you've added a word and checked the list a few times, you'll have memorized the correct spelling. You can then cross it off your list!

Words I Frequently Misspell

_____	_____
_____	_____
_____	_____
_____	_____
_____	_____
_____	_____
_____	_____
_____	_____

Sometimes, misspelling is not the problem. You're confused by sound-alike or look-alike words *(to, too, two).*

Try It

This message would get through spell check, but it has errors in word usage. Circle each incorrect word, and write the correct word above it.

Thanks for your inquiry about the pare of read shoes featured in our

catalog. The shoes are died to match the dress that is shown on the

same page. Many people order both and like to ware them together.

The shoes are on sail. If you'd like to by this item, you must first pay the

balance on your overdo account. We are not aloud to ship you knew

merchandise until you pay your passed do bill.

This version of the e-mail has the correct word written above the circled word it replaces.

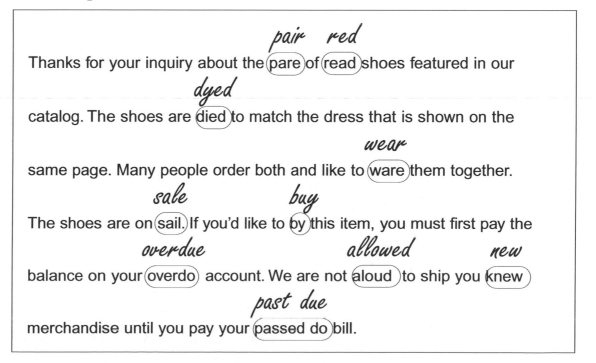

Did you find all of the look-alike and sound-alike words? If you missed any, check the list of sound-alikes below to help you choose the correct word.

Frequently Confused Words: Sound-Alikes and Look-Alikes

accept/except	**accept:** to receive, to agree *I accepted the terms of the contract.*	**except:** exclude; but *We have all the items you ordered except the down quilt.*
ad/add	**ad:** abbreviation for advertisement *The ad must be placed by 10:00 a.m.*	**add:** to perform a mathematical procedure *Please add six percent sales tax to the purchase price.*
addition/edition	**addition:** mathematical procedure; also *Do you want to order the matching earrings in addition to the necklace?*	**edition:** a particular version of a document *This is the third edition of the textbook.*
advice/advise	**advice:** recommendation; guidance *Can you give me some advice on a gift?*	**advise:** to recommend; to suggest *I'd advise you to give a gift certificate.*
affect/effect	**affect:** to influence *Your latest payment of $55.70 will affect the balance you own on this account.*	**effect:** an accomplishment; to bring about; being in full force *The summer sale will be in effect until August 1.*
aid/aide	**aid:** the act of helping *Our Web site should aid you in ordering online.*	**aide:** person acting as an assistant *The political candidates brought their campaign aides to the meeting.*
all ready/already	**all ready:** completed *The order is all ready to send.*	**already:** before; so soon *I have already sent an invoice.*
bare/bear	**bare:** naked *This cape is a perfect cover for bare arms on chilly nights.*	**bear:** a type of animal *The rug is made from bear skin.* **bear:** to hold up, support; to be accountable for *We cannot bear the responsibility for misuse.*
be/bee	**be:** a verb form; used as a helping verb *Our agents will be with you as soon as possible.*	**bee:** an insect *Customers enjoy our clover honey made by the wild bee.*
beside/besides	**beside:** next to *The price appears beside the product description.*	**besides:** in addition; also *Besides the camel-hair blazer, we sell a camel-hair overcoat.*
billed/build	**billed:** to present a statement of costs or charges *You have been billed for your entire order.*	**build:** to construct *All the parts are in the box, but you will have to build the model.*

brake/break	**brake:** a device for stopping or slowing motion *We are recalling all 2000 models because of a problem with the brake.*	**break:** to separate into parts; to smash *If you don't package the crystal carefully, it will break.*
buy/by	**buy:** to purchase *You have to buy the ink cartridges for the printer.*	**by:** next to; not later than *We hope to ship your order by Monday.*
choose/chose	**choose:** to select *You may choose either of the free gifts.*	**chose:** past tense of choose *Last year you chose to receive a cash rebate.*
complement/ compliment	**complement:** to complete *The red shoes will complement the outfit.*	**compliment:** to praise *I'd like to compliment you for your good work.*
continuously/ continually	**continuously:** uninterrupted or constant *The video is played continuously.*	**continually:** reoccurring often *We continually review and update our policies.*
do/due	**do:** to perform or execute *I was unable to do the work you described.*	**due:** owed as a debt; expected *Payment is due upon acceptance.*
dual/duel	**dual:** composed of two; a double purpose *The tote bag has dual compartments.*	**duel:** prearranged formal combat *We prefer to mediate your complaint, not engage in a duel with you.*
dyeing/dying	**dyeing:** coloring with a dye *I'm dyeing the shoes according to your instructions.*	**dying:** ceasing to live *The plant you purchased is dying because of poor care.*
envelop/envelope	**envelop:** to surround *We envelop the vase with foam to prevent breakage.*	**envelope:** container for a letter *Return your payment in the brown envelope we provided.*
ensure/insure	**ensure:** to make certain *We do everything to ensure your satisfaction.*	**insure:** to protect against financial loss *You can insure the building against fire damage.*
farther/further	**farther:** used to describe a measure of physical distance *Our Connecticut store is farther from you than our New York store.*	**further:** used to describe advancement of a non-physical distance *We are further along than we thought.*
for/fore/four	**for:** preposition used to indicate aim, object, purpose, or recipient of an action *We will be happy to process the return for you.* **fore:** before; in front of *This scale-model schooner comes with fore-and-aft rigging.*	**four:** numeral *Please send me four copies of the book.*

Frequently Confused Words: Sound-Alikes and Look-Alikes *(continued)*

forth/fourth	**forth:** forward in time, place, and order *Despite setbacks, we are moving forth.*	**fourth:** a number *This is the fourth time I've asked you to take me off your mailing list.*
hear/here	**hear:** to perceive sound *Despite the noise, I was able to hear your complaint.*	**here:** at or in this place *Click here to learn more.*
hole/whole	**hole:** an opening *To attach, insert the string in the hole.*	**whole:** entire; complete *I will tell you the whole story.*
knew/new	**knew:** was aware of *He knew of the product defect.*	**new:** recent; unfamiliar *The raincoat is a new addition to our catalog.*
loose/lose	**loose:** not tight *After the accident, the car's bumper was loose.*	**lose:** to misplace *I frequently lose my keys.*
made/maid	**made:** constructed; forced *All of our products are made in the United States.*	**maid:** a servant *The rate includes daily maid service.*
mail/male	**mail:** postal material *The mail is delivered in the morning.*	**male:** a man or boy *Please indicate whether the applicant is male or female.*
maybe/may be	**maybe:** perhaps; possible *He said that maybe the order would be processed today.*	**may be:** might be; could be *We may be able to build a product that meets your needs.*
morning/ mourning	**morning:** before noon *The stockholders' meeting is scheduled for the morning.*	**mourning:** period of grieving *We are still mourning the death of our company's president.*
no/know	**no:** not any; negative *We have no excuse for misplacing your order.*	**know:** to have knowledge of *We know we can handle your order promptly and efficiently.*
overdo/overdue	**overdo:** to do too much *If you overdo your workout, your muscles will be sore.*	**overdue:** beyond the expected time *Your payment is 30 days overdue.*
pair/pare/pear	**pair:** two of a kind *The socks you returned were not a pair.* **pare:** to peel *The cake will taste sour if you don't pare the apples before baking.*	**pear:** a fruit *The pear was not ripe.*
passed/past	**passed:** overtook; moved ahead; went beyond; surpassed *Our new truck passed all the safety tests.*	**past:** an earlier time *Those software failures were in the past.*

peak/peek	**peak:** to approach the top or maximum *Hotel rates peak during tourist season.*	**peek:** to glance quickly *I peeked at your order but didn't review it carefully.*
personal/ personnel	**personal:** private *We consider your medical history to be a personal matter.*	**personnel:** employees *All of our accounting personnel will work on the project.*
plain/plane	**plain:** simple *The black dress is plain but elegant.*	**plane:** airplane *The plane has a business class section.*
pray/prey	**pray:** to utter a prayer; make an urgent plea *We pray that you'll make a contribution to this worthwhile charity.*	**prey:** an animal hunted for food; to victimize *The salesman was fired because he preyed on elderly couples.*
precede/proceed	**precede:** to go before *The 1992 and 1994 editions precede the current one.*	**proceed:** to continue *I got permission to proceed with the transaction.*
principal/ principle	**principal:** head of a school *Mr. Jones was named principal of Maywood Elementary School.* **principle:** a rule; standard of good behavior *The decision was based on principle, not profit.*	**principal:** a sum of money *You paid back the principal of your loan.* **principal:** main *The principal reason for the meeting is to plan a strategy.*
read/red	**read:** to have examined or grasped written material *He read our mission statement on our Web site.*	**red:** color *The coat comes in black or red.*
sale/sail	**sale:** the exchange of goods and services for money *The sale of the business took place in March.* **sail:** to travel by water *The ship with your goods is scheduled to sail on Monday.*	**sale:** disposal of goods at a lower price *We are having a sale on all of our computers.*
scene/seen	**scene:** part of a play *The carpenters built a set for that scene.*	**seen:** perceived with the eye *The buyer has seen the same dress in other stores.*
seams/seems	**seams:** lines formed by sewing together fabric *This model sewing machine will guide you to sew straight seams.*	**seems:** appears *Resolving your problem seems simple.*
sew/so	**sew:** to stitch *A beginner could sew this dress.*	**so:** therefore *He left a message, so I returned his call.*

sight/cite/site	**sight:** the act of seeing *Customers were excited by the sight of the new model.* **site:** a location *To register, visit our Web site.*	**cite:** to quote *Please cite all of your sources of information.*
stationary/ stationery	**stationary:** not movable *The stationary pedestals support the office's plants and sculptures.*	**stationery:** writing paper *Our most popular product is stationery.*
than/then	**than:** compared with *The 1,000DS has more storage space than the 200DS.*	**then:** at that time; next in time *First we will bill you, then we will ship your order.*
their/there/they're	**their:** belonging to them *We used their research in our book.* **there:** in that place *Place your returned items over there, on the counter.*	**they're:** contraction for they are *They're the ones who registered for the course.*
thorough/through/ threw/thru	**thorough:** complete *We gave your complaint a thorough review.* **threw:** tossed *Because your son threw the ball, your insurance will not pay to replace the window.*	**through:** from beginning to the end *We couldn't make our way through the contract.* **thru:** informal for *through* *You can order food at our drive-thru window.*
to/two/too	**to:** in the direction of *We sent it to the buyer.* **two:** numeral *We shipped two of the items you ordered.*	**too:** also *Check out our new model, too.*
undo/undue	**undo:** to reverse *I'm sorry that we can't undo our error.*	**undue:** excessive; not just or proper *We determined the damage was caused by undue force.*
waist/waste	**waist:** middle of the body *The size 10 dress has a 32-inch waist.*	**waste:** to consume carelessly *Your old dishwasher wastes energy and water.*
wait/weight	**wait:** rest in anticipation *We wait for the newest model.*	**weight:** a measure of heaviness *The shipping and handling fees are based on the weight of the package.*
waive/wave	**waive:** to give up a claim *We'll waive the interest charges.*	**wave:** a surge or rush *All of the robots were purchased by the first wave of customers.*
where/wear	**where:** at or in what place *Where is your store located?*	**wear:** to dress in *What size shoes do you normally wear?*

Frequently Confused Words: Sound-Alikes and Look-Alikes (continued)

weather/whether	**weather:** state of atmospheric conditions *Our Web site has a link to the local weather forecast.*	**whether:** if *I'm wondering whether I can return the item I purchased online.*
we're/ were	**we're:** contraction for we are *We're the leading manufacturer of computer chips.*	**were:** form of the verb "to be" *Both companies were founded in 1999.*
wood/would	**wood:** lumber *The entire chair is made of wood.*	**would:** auxiliary form of helping verb *I would have sent you a refund if you had returned the jacket.*
write/right	**write:** to form letters/words *Please write to us if you have other questions.*	**right:** correct; direction *It broke because you did not use it the right way.* *Turn right at the stop sign.*
your/you're	**your:** belonging to you *Bring your identification when you register.*	**you're:** contraction for you are *You're the winner of the contest.*

Practice 5.1—
Choose the Correct Word

Write the correct word above the pair of words. For answers to **Practice 5.1**, see page 102.

To: James.Reiss@mailman.com
From: CustSvc@FastypePrinting.com
Subject: Answers to your questions about Fastype Printing services

Dear James Reiss:

Thanks for your e-mail inquiring about our printing services. Yes, we do

print **stationary/stationery**. It is one of the **principal/principle** services

that we offer. We will be glad to develop a logo for you. Our price for

designing the logo and letterhead, as well as printing 1,000 sheets of

stationery/stationary and **envelops/envelopes**, is $500.

Please tell me **where/wear** you'd like me to send the contract. I will

mail/male it to you. If you **except/accept** these terms and would like to

precede/proceed, please sign and return the contract. That will

insure/ensure quick service.

Sincerely,

Jean Berg
Fastype Printing

Practice 5.2—
Find the Misused Word and Replace It with the Correct Word

Circle the misspelled words and write the correct words above them. For answers to **Practice 5.2**, see page 103.

1. We do not have any vacancies for the weaks you requested.

2. During off-peek periods, we accept reservations for shorter stays.

3. Hear is the answer to the question you asked in your e-mail.

4. Bee sure to click on the box to the left of the school's name, and then

   click the "ad" button to list additional schools.

5. You do not have to weight to file your application.

6. Please go to our policies page for more information regarding Web

   cite security.

7. The procedures are different for foreign students seeking financial aide.

8. I'm sorry that you are having trouble accessing our site in the evenings,

   our peek hours. Please try in the mourning when usage is lower.

9. The sail price for the computer is no longer in affect.

10. The humidity in the air will effect how long the tree lasts.

11. We received too e-mail messages from you regarding the soymilk maker.

    Hear is my explanation four the watery milk.

12. I believe you will have know problem with the delivery, but due let us no if

    we can bee of further assistance.

Make Your Own "Cheat Sheet" of Words You Often Confuse

Did you miss any words in **Practice 5.2**? Are there others on the list that you frequently confuse? Enter them in the chart below to create your personal list of commonly confused words. We've given you an example of easily confused words: *compliment* and *complement.* Refer to your "Cheat Sheet" as you write your e-mail responses.

Commonly Confused Words	Definition
compliment/ complement	compliment: praise *I'd rather get a bonus than receive a compliment.* complement: complete or make whole *The necklace is a complement to the earrings.*

The correct word appears above the incorrect word.

To: James.Reiss@mailman.com
From: CustSvc@FastypePrinting.com
Subject: Answers to your questions about Fastype Printing services

Dear James Reiss:

Thanks for your e-mail inquiring about our printing services. Yes, we do

stationery   *principal*
print **stationary/stationery**. It is one of the **principal/principle** services

that we offer. We will be glad to develop a logo for you. Our price for

designing the logo and letterhead, as well as printing 1,000 sheets of

stationery   *envelopes*
stationery/stationary and **envelops/envelopes**, is $500.

where
Please tell me **where/ wear** you'd like me to send the contract. I will

mail   *accept*
mail/male it to you. If you **except/accept** these terms and would like to

proceed
precede/proceed, please sign and return the contract. That will

ensure
insure/ensure quick service.

Sincerely,

Jean Berg
Fastype Printing

Answers to Practice 5.2—
Find the Misused Word and Replace It with the Correct Word

The correct word appears above the incorrect word.

1. We do not have any vacancies for the *weeks* (weaks) you requested.

2. For off-*peak* (peek) periods, we accept reservations for shorter stays.

3. *Here* (Hear) is the answer to the question you asked in your e-mail.

4. *Be* (Bee) sure to click on the box to the left of the school's name, and then click the *"add"* ("ad") button to list additional schools.

5. You do not have to *wait* (weight) to file your application.

6. Please go to our policies page for more information regarding Web *site* (cite) security.

7. The procedures are different for foreign students seeking financial *aid* (aide.)

8. I'm sorry that you are having trouble accessing our site in the evenings, our *peak* (peek) hours. Please try in the *morning* (mourning) when usage is lower.

9. The *sale* (sail) price for the computer is no longer in *effect* (affect.)

10. The humidity in the air will *affect* (effect) how long the tree lasts.

11. We received *two* (too) e-mail messages from you regarding the soymilk maker. *Here* (Hear) is my explanation *for* (four) the watery milk.

12. I believe you will have *no* (know) problem with the delivery, but *do* (due) let us *know* (no) if we can *be* (bee) of further assistance.

Chapter 6
Punctuate Correctly

In this chapter, you'll learn punctuation rules for the most common punctuation marks in customer service e-mail messages:

Period
Comma
Apostrophe
Semicolon
Colon

Some people really like to study punctuation rules. They are proud to know the obscure exception to the 18th comma rule or how the use of the dash has evolved over the past 200 years. But for the rest of us, punctuation rules can seem like a weird interest of teachers and copyeditors. And when we're writing e-mail quickly, we hardly think we need to review our punctuation. After all, can't our customers understand our e-mails even if our punctuation isn't perfect? Is punctuation really important in the online world?

Yes, punctuation is important, and it will continue to be important in spite of the tremendous changes e-mail has brought to business writing. Punctuation affects meaning. An agent who doesn't know how to use commas and semicolons might make the following mistake when explaining the location of the company service centers: *We have service centers in Detroit, Michigan, Chicago, Illinois, and Bloomington, Indiana.* This punctuation looks wrong and is wrong. What's more, it seems that that agent doesn't know the difference between a city and a state! Here's the correct punctuation: *We have service centers in Detroit, Michigan; Chicago, Illinois; and Bloomington, Indiana.*

Punctuation marks carry meaning. They tell us to stop, to pause, to get ready to read an example, or to get ready to read a quotation. Correct punctuation makes it easier for customers to understand what we're telling them in e-mail messages and, therefore, makes it more likely that they won't write to us a second time asking the same question.

Sending correctly punctuated e-mail gives customers confidence in the information you provide. (And, yes, punctuation errors in e-mail make customers wonder whether you really know what you're talking about!)

Rules for Using the Period

1. Use a period to end a complete sentence.

   Example   I've included the shipping information for your SupraToy.com order.

2. Use a period at the end of an indirect question.

   Example   You asked whether you could pay your bill for service online.

3. Within parentheses, use a period when the information inside the parentheses is a complete sentence.

   Example   You must include a check for the full amount due when you send back your completed request form. (You may also pay by money order.)

Practice 6.1—
Use the Period Correctly

Add periods to these sentences. For answers to **Practice 6.1**, see page 119.

1. We have charged $26.84 to your credit card (Please note that this charge will appear on your credit card statement from HOMESTYLE ENTERPRISES)

2. You asked how to use two different credit cards to register eight people for this course We sincerely appreciate your business and look forward to seeing you online again soon

3. We asked you whether you had tried to complete our online application form

4. If you fail to enclose payment, we cannot process your request

Rules for Using the Comma

There are more rules for using commas than any busy agent will want to memorize. The list of rules we're offering here isn't comprehensive; it's selective. We've selected the comma rules you're most likely to need when you answer customers' e-mail.

1.   Use a comma to separate the items in a list or series. The items may be words, phrases, or clauses.

Example   You can shop online for vacuum cleaner tools, bags, and replacement power cords.

Example   Please access our online billing center at http://www.support.webland.com to review your invoice, provide an alternate method of payment, or make any other requests using a service ticket.

Example   Our online billing center can verify the date we sent the bill, the amount of the bill, and your billing address.

2.   Use commas to set off the name or title of the person you are addressing in the sentence.

Example   Thank you, Frances, for your e-mail to the Xerox Office Printing E-Mail Support Team.

Example   We are sorry to tell you, Linda, that Sandy Hill Bank does not offer a Visa Business Card.

3.   Use a comma to set off introductory words, phrases, or clauses.

Example   In addition, we will charge you an application fee each time the logo is applied to an item.

Example   Again, I will try to make the necessary arrangements to remove you from this list if that is what you want.

Example   Please remember, technical questions require more processing time because we may need to contact our technical staff for resolution.

4. Use a comma to set off non-essential phrases or clauses. A non-essential clause can be removed from the sentence without changing the meaning of the main clause.

Example   Gift certificates can be ordered by e-mail, if you would like, or by telephone.

Example   You could choose the Randolph RG1067SC drum set, if you play rock or jazz, for $389.99, which would be in your price range.

5. Use a comma before the coordinating conjunction that separates the clauses in a compound sentence, a sentence that contains two independent clauses. These words are coordinating conjunctions: *and, but, or, nor, for, yet, so.*

Example   I would like to buy the QV30 Carrietta digital camera, but I can't find any place to purchase it in the Washington, D.C., area.

Example   We can give you the medical advice you need, or we can assist you in finding the medical advice.

Example   FAF Group has a "print before you submit the online form" feature at its Web site, but I could not find this feature at your site.

Practice 6.2—
Use the Comma Correctly

Add commas to these sentences. For answers to **Practice 6.2,** see page 119.

1. We have also made changes to our flight schedules to New York London and Boston.

2. If so I suggest that you add this feature to your site in the future.

3. To be eligible you must complete your Data Confirmation Report which shows all the information you've entered on your application then submit the Data Confirmation Report online.

4. You can also view your order status order history or account management information from this page.

5. I like seeing all of my accounts using ViewNet but I found the system to be riddled with problems.

6. As always InterCredit is improving all aspects of our service to keep customers satisfied.

7. We value your association with the Hostel Travel Club Anthony and look forward to your future participation.

8. You can use the examples found on our Web site as an aid to formulating your own searches and you can follow these quick tips to getting started.

9. Call our Registration Services Department toll-free at 800-555-8056 Monday through Friday if you have any questions or if we can be of further assistance.

10. Please contact our Communications Department Jay with your questions about your domestic travel plans.

Rules for Using the Apostrophe

The apostrophe has two jobs. First, the apostrophe shows where letters have been left out in a contraction such as *that's*. In *that's*, the apostrophe replaces the letter *i*. If the apostrophe weren't there, we would write *that is*. Second, the apostrophe shows possession. To show that the *office* belongs to the *director*, we would write *director's office*.

1. Use an apostrophe to form the possessive of a singular or plural noun. Place the apostrophe between the noun and the *s* to show possession with a singular noun. Place the apostrophe after the *s* with a plural noun.

   Example   We need the doctor's report by September 30, 2003.

   Example   You can find our staff members' phone numbers listed in the company directory at our Web site.

2. If two or more people or groups each possess something, place an apostrophe after each one's name.

   Example   Customer Service's and Management's plans are to hire more people to help out during the holiday season.

3. If two or more people or groups possess something together, place an apostrophe only after the last name.

   Example   Carolyn Smith and Lauren Warren's job-sharing contract specifies that they will work 20 hours per week in total on the Customer Care Web site.

4. Add only an apostrophe to form the possessive of a plural noun ending in the letter *s*.

   Example   For more information on our publishers' solutions, please follow the "For Publishers" links at our Web site.

   Example   By the owners' choice, all the condominiums in the building are closed for a week during February for maintenance and cleaning.

5. Add *'s* to a singular noun ending in *s,* such as *bus,* if the possessive adds a syllable to the word.

Example   We were late because the airport shuttle bus's front tire became flat and we had to wait for the driver to change the tire.

Add only an apostrophe (don't add an s) if the extra syllable would give the word too many "s" sounds and make it hard to pronounce.

Example   Weiss' claim that he was injured was highly suspicious to the judge.

6. Use an apostrophe to show where letters have been left out or a contraction.

Example   I'm interested in ordering your products, inscribed with our corporate logo, for my company.

Example   The medical report should show why you can't work.

7. **Watch out for one important exception to the rule for using an apostrophe to show possession! DO NOT use an apostrophe for the possessive form of the word *it*.**

Example   The jacket has two pocket flaps, not pockets. You cannot open either of its pocket flaps or you will tear the jacket.

Example   If you have trouble removing the vacuum cover, place a screwdriver under its lip and twist.

DO use an apostrophe for *it's*, the contraction for *it is*.

Example   Maybe I am just having bad luck, but it's taking way too long to conduct my business.

Example   The jacket can be returned if it's defective.

Practice 6.3—
Use the Apostrophe Correctly

Add apostrophes to these sentences where they are necessary. For answers to **Practice 6.3**, see page 120.

1. Because these employees are from two separate groups, Ill be using two credit cards to pay their airfare.

2. I need to follow up on a financial aid issue that is confusing. The students name is Lucas Kottasall.

3. Ive applied for a pension, and I thought Id sent you everything you needed to process my application.

4. With Pearsalls enhanced online services, you can now search our catalogs by topic or other key word.

5. If you wish to search only one of the categories, make sure its selected at the top of the search form.

6. I havent had a Hillwood Credit Union ATM card for at least two to three years.

7. Your companys address has been corrected in our system, as you requested.

8. Our mens fall 2005 catalog and our womens fall 2005 catalog have a photograph of a flag on the cover.

9. You must first locate the facility by referring to the map weve given you, then by looking up its mail stop and zip code.

Rules for Using the Semicolon

Think of the semicolon as a really powerful comma, strong enough to place between two groups of words that could be sentences by themselves.

1. Use a semicolon to separate two independent clauses—a group of words with a subject and verb that makes sense by itself—not joined by a conjunction.

    Example   Our International Friends Poster is available in Spanish; the item number is FA9059.

    Example   I'm sorry to be writing to you under these tragic circumstances; I trust that you will understand why we have taken these extreme, but necessary, measures.

2. Use a semicolon between two independent clauses joined by a transition word such as *therefore, however, consequently,* or *moreover.*

    Example   I am unable to address your particular issue; however, I can refer you to the proper contact at our company to assist you with your needs.

    Example   We have also reduced the number of people on our management team; however, on a positive note, we will be increasing our project management capacity in Africa and the Far East.

3. Use a semicolon to separate the items in a series when the items already include commas.

    Example   We invite you to visit us at our retail outlets in Miami, Florida; Chicago, Illinois; or Phoenix, Arizona.

Practice 6.4—
Use the Semicolon Correctly

Add semicolons to these sentences. For answers to **Practice 6.4**, see page 121.

1. Many clients find the break-even point to be between $20,000 and $30,000 however that break-even number differs from client to client.

2. Supply the pick-up and drop-off dates select a car rental company from the drop-down list.

3. Choose from these warm fleece items for kids: V-neck pullover, in blue or green elastic-waist pants, in blue, green, or black and stocking cap, in blue or black.

4. I'd like to rent a Chrysler PT Cruiser on my next trip I don't want to rent another Ford Explorer!

5. I do not know the whole situation however, I have tested your e-mail account personally, and it is fine.

6. We have some effective tips on cleaning the filter please visit our web site at www.tropicalfish.com/cleantips.html.

7. If you're interested in working for us, please contact Lynette Rico, communications director Marjorie Folger, human resources director and Jerry Agnew, webmaster.

Rules for Using the Colon

A colon says to a reader, "Here comes a list or an example." The colon is easy to use correctly if you remember that the words to the left of the colon usually must be a full sentence, not merely part of a sentence.

For example, this use of the colon is WRONG. *Our company hopes customers will: complete our online survey, register for the prize drawing, and sign up for our free newsletter.* This sentence is punctuated incorrectly because the colon follows the words *Our company hopes customers will,* but those words are NOT a full sentence. Here is the CORRECT use of the colon in this sentence. *Our company hopes customers will visit our Web site for many reasons: to complete our online survey, to register for the prize drawing, and to sign up for our free newsletter.*

1. Use a colon to introduce a list. Be sure the group of words to the left of the colon is a full sentence (an independent clause).

    Example   The end table you asked about has many convenient features: deep drawers, legs on casters, and a durable finish.

    Example   Unfortunately, we no longer carry the following catalog items: pogo sticks, unicycles, and mini-trampolines.

2. Use a colon to introduce an example, illustration, or explanation of the idea to the left of the colon.

    Example   The party room rental contract stipulated an important condition: the client will provide tablecloths.

    Example   You can track the status of your order online by visiting our home page: www.XYZcompany.com.

    Example   Our refund policy is clear: you may return the merchandise within 30 days of receipt for a full refund of merchandise and shipping charges.

Practice 6.5—
Use the Colon Correctly

Add colons to these sentences. For answers to **Practice 6.5**, see page 121.

1. With product inquiries, please call one of our regional offices Midwest Region at 800-555-9865, West Coast Region at 800-555-3687, or East Coast Region at 800-555-4113.

2. We have two ways of charging for Spanish language tutoring an hourly charge of $10 or a daily charge of $50.

3. I want to purchase three of the titles I see in your list of helpful books on spelling *Learn to Spell, Spell Correctly without Memorizing,* and *Spelling Tips for Poor Spellers.*

4. Customers cannot find the serial number strip underneath the product we received five phone calls last week asking for help finding the number.

5. We charge a one-time set-up fee based on the number of stitches it takes to create your logo $95 for 8,000 stitches.

6. The following pages will allow you to provide important rental information the driver's name, frequent traveler programs, corporate plans, or other rate options.

Punctuating the E-Mail Greeting: Choose a Comma, a Colon, or a Dash

Most customer service e-mail begins by addressing the customer by name. You have several options for punctuating the greeting:

Dear Mr. Campi: (colon)

Hello, Allan -- (comma/dash combination)

Dear Allan, (comma)

Hi Mrs. Davis, (comma)

Hello Robert, (comma)

Hello Gerry -- (dash)

So, which is the best punctuation choice? All are acceptable, but each one carries a slightly different tone or level of formality. Most writers agree that the colon is the most formal way of punctuating a greeting. *Dear Mr. Campi*: is the greeting we would use when writing a print business letter. Punctuating with a colon carries some of the business letter's formality. The comma is just slightly more casual than the colon. *Dear Allan,* is the greeting we would choose in a personal letter or in casual business writing. The most informal choice is the dash, by itself *(Hello Gerry --)* or used with a comma after *hello (Hello, Gerry --)*. Use the dash in your greeting when you have permission or support for writing in a casual style.

Where necessary, add periods, commas, apostrophes, semicolons, and colons to this message. Also add capital letters, if necessary. Remember, there may be more than one correct way to punctuate this message. Compare your answers to **Practice 6.6** with ours on page 122.

To: Apatt@dictio.com
From: Terry.Capanski@CountryFurnitureCustSvc.com
Subject: Thompson day bed and trundle information

Hello Amanda Patterson

Thank you for your interest in the Thompson daybed and trundle the daybed is not available for viewing at the retail location you asked about. Our outlets inventory varies daily and we cannot advise if and when the daybed would be available at an outlet store. Please contact your local Country Furniture Outlet for assistance. We have several Country Furniture Outlet stores in your area at Holland Mall in Frostville, NY at Boxwood Mall in Clarence, NY and at Warren Shopping Center in Carter, NY.

To answer your question about mattress size the daybed and trundle both accommodate a standard twin-size mattress. The daybed stores its trundle neatly beneath its frame. We also sell frames for larger mattresses the Sweetwater frame can accommodate a full-size mattress and the Coverley bed frame accommodates a queen-size mattress. Its a good idea to look at a variety of frames before you choose one

The beds may be returned within 30 days for a full refund of merchandise and shipping charges. After 30 days we will replace or refund your purchase against manufacturers defects however we cannot refund your purchase if you damage the merchandise while trying to assemble it.

You may order your bed online call our Sales Department at 800-555-5176 or stop in at one of our retail outlets. Please continue to look at our catalog online and please contact us if we may be of any further assistance.

Regards

Terry Capanski
Customer Service
Country Furniture

Answers to Practice 6.1—Use the Period Correctly

Here is the correct punctuation for these sentences.

1. We have charged $26.84 to your credit card. (Please note that this charge will appear on your credit card statement from HOMESTYLE ENTERPRISES.)

2. You asked how to use two different credit cards to register eight people for this course.

4. We sincerely appreciate your business and look forward to seeing you online again soon.

5. We asked you whether you had tried to complete our online application form.

6. If you fail to enclose payment, we cannot process your request.

Answers to Practice 6.2—Use the Comma Correctly

Here is the correct punctuation for these sentences.

1. We have also made changes to our flight schedules to New York, London, and Boston.

2. If so, I suggest that you add this feature to your site in the future.

3. To be eligible, you must complete your Data Confirmation Report, which shows all the information you've entered on your application, then submit the Data Confirmation Report online.

4. You can also view your order status, order history, or account management information from this page.

5. I like seeing all of my accounts using ViewNet, but I found the system to be riddled with problems.

6. As always, InterCredit is improving all aspects of our service to keep customers satisfied.

7. We value your association with the Hostel Travel Club, Anthony, and look forward to your future participation.

8. You can use the examples found on our Web site as an aid to formulating your own searches, and you can follow these quick tips to getting started.

9. Call our Registration Services Department toll free at 800-555-8056, Monday through Friday, if you have any questions or if we can be of further assistance.

10. Please contact our Communications Department, Jay, with your questions about your domestic travel plans.

Answers to Practice 6.3—Use the Apostrophe Correctly

Here is the correct punctuation for these sentences.

1. Because these employees are from two separate groups, I'll be using two credit cards to pay their airfare.

2. I need to follow up on a financial aid issue that is confusing. The student's name is Lucas Kottasall.

3. I've applied for a pension, and I thought I'd sent you everything you needed to process my application.

4. With Pearsall's enhanced online services, you can now search our catalogs by topic or other key word.

5. If you wish to search only one of the categories, make sure it's selected at the top of the search form.

6. I haven't had a Hillwood Credit Union ATM card for at least two to three years.

7. Your company's address has been corrected in our system, as you requested.

8. Our men's fall 2005 catalog and our women's fall 2005 catalog have a photograph of a flag on the cover.

9. You must first locate the facility by referring to the map we've given you, then by looking up its mail stop and zip code.

Answers to Practice 6.4—Use the Semicolon Correctly

Here is the correct punctuation for these sentences.

1. Many clients find the break-even point to be between $20,000 and $30,000; however, that break-even number differs from client to client.

2. Supply the pick-up and drop-off dates; select a car rental company from the drop-down list.

3. Choose from these warm fleece items for kids: V-neck pullover, in blue or green; elastic-waist pants, in blue, green, or black; and stocking cap, in blue or black.

4. I'd like to rent a Chrysler PT Cruiser on my next trip; I don't want to rent another Ford Explorer.

5. I do not know the whole situation; however, I have tested your e-mail account personally, and it is fine.

6. We have some effective tips on cleaning the filter; please visit our Web site at www.tropicalfish.com/cleantips.html.

7. If you're interested in working for us, please contact Lynette Rico, communications director; Marjorie Folger, human resources director; and Jerry Agnew, webmaster.

Answers to Practice 6.5—Use the Colon Correctly

Here is the correct punctuation for these sentences.

1. With product inquiries, please call one of our regional offices: Midwest Region at 800–555–9865, West Coast Region at 800–555–3687, or East Coast Region at 800–555–4113.

2. We have two ways of charging for Spanish language tutoring: an hourly charge of $10 or a daily charge of $50.

3. I want to purchase three of the titles I see in your list of helpful books on spelling: *Learn to Spell, Spell Correctly without Memorizing,* and *Spelling Tips for Poor Spellers.*

4. Customers cannot find the serial number strip underneath the product: we received five phone calls last week asking for help finding the number.

5. We charge a one-time set-up fee based on the number of stitches it takes to create your logo: $95 for 8,000 stitches.

6. The following pages will allow you to provide important rental information: the driver's name, frequent traveler programs, corporate plans, or other rate options.

To: Apatt@dictio.com
From: Terry.Capanski@CountryFurnitureCustSvc.com
Subject: Thompson day bed and trundle information

Hello Amanda Patterson,

Thank you for your interest in the Thompson Daybed and Trundle. The daybed is not available for viewing at the retail location you asked about. Our outlet's inventory varies daily, and we cannot advise if and when the daybed would be available at an outlet store. Please contact your local Country Furniture Outlet for assistance. We have several Country Furniture Outlet stores in your area: at Holland Mall in Frostville, NY; at Boxwood Mall in Clarence, NY; and at Warren Shopping Center in Carter, NY.

To answer your question about mattress size, the daybed and trundle both accommodate a standard twin-size mattress. The daybed stores its trundle neatly beneath its frame. We also sell frames for larger mattresses. The Sweetwater frame can accommodate a full-size mattress, and the Coverley bed frame accommodates a queen-size mattress. It's a good idea to look at a variety of frames before you choose one.

The beds may be returned within 30 days for a full refund of merchandise and shipping charges. After 30 days, we will replace or refund your purchase against manufacturer's defects; however, we cannot refund your purchase if you damage the merchandise while trying to assemble it.

You may order your bed online; call our Sales Department at 800-555-5176, or stop in at one of our retail outlets. Please continue to look at our catalog online, and please contact us if we may be of any further assistance.

Regards,

Terry Capanski
Country Furniture
Customer Service

Chapter 7—
Write for Global Customers

In this chapter, you'll learn how to

Identify idioms that can confuse global customers
Replace idioms with literal expressions
Write customer service e-mail that is sensitive to cultural differences
Write gender-neutral e-mail

When we think about the importance of "globalizing" customer service writing, we think about a story our friend told us. Our friend went into Sears and asked the clerk where he could find shoe trees. The clerk responded with a confused look as he repeated, "Shoe tree?" in heavily accented English, then directed our friend to the gardening department.

English contains thousands of colloquial expressions, idioms, culturally specific references, and coined words. These words and phrases can confuse non-native English speakers.

The Internet and e-mail now enable your customers to reach you from any part of the globe. And even local customers may not be native English speakers. In this chapter you'll learn how to write e-mail messages that are accessible to all your customers, regardless of location, native language, or sex.

Replace Idioms with Words Everyone Will Understand

Idioms—or idiomatic expressions—are commonly used words or phrases whose meaning cannot be derived from the individual words. Think of the literal meaning of *chairperson* and the image that idiom might evoke for a non-native English speaker. What images come to mind when you think of these idioms—*spread ourselves too thin, think outside the box, get ahead of myself, change my mind?*

Some idioms are easy to spot and edit out of our e-mails, but many idioms have become so common that we use them without even realizing that they are idioms and may be confusing to non-native English speakers. You will probably find that it is virtually impossible to write more than a few sentences without using idioms such as *about time, by the way,* or *as well as.*

Cultural Confusion—Who's John Hancock?

Because they are culturally specific, some idioms are confusing. For example, idiomatic expressions derived from sports like football or baseball are particularly confusing for people unfamiliar with the sport. These culturally specific idioms include *touch base, in the ball park,* and *caught off guard.*

We commonly use references to popular books, TV, movies, and history in our speech and in our writing. Non-native English speakers won't understand such phrases as the following:

- You've found the *Catch-22* in our regulations.

- I agree that the procedures were *Mickey Mouse.*

- Put your *John Hancock* on the contract and send it back to me.

Here's an example of how difficult it is to figure out cultural references when you are not part of the culture. How would you respond if you received this e-mail from the owner of a British bed-and-breakfast you were considering visiting?

Each cottage is equipped and furnished to the very highest standards using Liberty and Sanderson fabrics. All buildings are on the 1840 tythe map.

Practice 7.1—
Find Substitutes for Idiomatic Expressions

This **Practice** contains idioms that a global customer might not understand. In the **Literal Expressions** column, write a replacement for the idiom. This **Practice** is quite long, so you might want to do it with a colleague. For answers to **Practice 7.1**, see page 145.

Idiomatic Expressions	Literal Expressions
24/7	
a snap	
a win-win	
about time	
across the board	
ahead of time	
all at once	
all day long	
as a rule	
as far as	
as soon as	
as usual	
as well as	
at a loss	
at fault	
at last	
bar none	
before you know it	
bend over backwards	
best bet	
bottom line	
brand new	
bread and butter	
brush up	
by the way	
caught off guard	
chairperson	
change hands	

Idiomatic Expressions

change one's mind

close out

cut back

cut corners

cut rate

double-check

down the road

dud

fair play

fallen through the cracks

feel free

figure out

fill the bill

first come first served

flying off the shelf

from scratch

gain ground

get a break

get in touch with

get off the ground

give the go ahead

give the green light

go through with

hands-on experience

headhunter

hitting the stores

hot deal

in black and white

in charge of

in lieu of

in short supply

in stock

in the ball park

in the long run

in the works

Literal Expressions

Idiomatic Expressions	Literal Expressions
it goes without saying	
keep track of	
layaway plan	
let things slide	
level playing field	
more than meets the eye	
on hand	
on the go	
on the road	
paperwork	
printed matter	
rain check	
relish the thought	
rest assured	
right up our alley	
run out	
run short	
sell like hotcakes	
short supply	
snap up	
spell out	
spread ourselves too thin	
stack up	
taken aback	
tall order	
test the waters	
think outside the box	
to the letter	
touch base	
up and running	
weed out	
wrap up	

Create Your Own "Cheat Sheet"

Review the list of idioms in **Practice 7.1.** Mark those expressions you use frequently. Then, copy them into the **Frequently Used Idioms** list. As you write e-mail to customers, you may find other idioms to add to this list. Keep this list handy so you can refer it when you write e-mails.

Frequently Used Idioms	Literal Expressions

Practice 7.2—
Edit to Remove Idiomatic Expressions

Here is a customer service agent's e-mail response to a customer's inquiry about where to purchase a Photopro 680 digital camera in the Washington, D.C., area. Idioms and phrases that might be difficult for a non-native English speaker are in **bold**. Edit this e-mail by substituting literal expressions in the space above the idiom. For answers to **Practice 7.2**, see page 148.

To: naveed@worldmail.com
From: CustomerService@Camerashops.com
Subject: Re: Where to buy Photopro 680 Digital in Washington, D.C.

Dear Naveed,

Thank you for your e-mail about the difficulty of finding a Photopro 680 digital camera in the Washington, D.C., area. We are sorry that you have not been able to locate this camera in a store in your area. We were **caught off guard** by the demand for this camera. They are **flying off the shelves** so they are **in short supply. Rest assured** that we are working hard to see that stores will have them **in stock just as soon as** we can.

The Walmart in your area should have them **on hand** shortly. You might also be interested in our **brand new** Photopro 780 camera that will be **hitting the stores** soon. I think that you'll find that this new camera **stacks up well** against higher-priced cameras.

Sincerely,

Jack
Customer Service, Camera Shops

Practice 7.3—
Find and Replace Idioms

This e-mail from a customer service agent contains idiomatic phrases that might confuse a non-native English speaker. Circle the idioms and write a replacement above each idiom. For answers to **Practice 7.3**, see page 149.

To: Marvelle@worldmail.com
From: Rita@Tranco.com
Subject: Re: Tranco coffee maker problem

Dear Marvelle,

Thanks for contacting us about your problem with your Tranco coffee maker. Printed matter explaining how to use the coffee maker should have been included. I'm attaching the instructions to this e-mail. Using the coffee maker is a snap. The instructions spell out the procedure for brewing coffee. If you follow the instructions for brewing coffee to the letter, the coffee maker will be up and running before you know it.

It goes without saying that we are very sorry that you were inconvenienced. As a rule, instructions are put inside every box.

Sincerely,

Rita
Tranco Coffee

Internationalize Dates, Times, and Numbers

When you provide information that involves numbers—dates, times, weights, measurements, or temperatures—remember that the systems and conventions that we use in the United States are not universal.

- In the United States, the convention for expressing the date is *month/day/year*. But many countries express the date as *day/month/year*. The international standard for expressing the date is *year/month/day*. To avoid confusion, write out dates: *January 10, 2005.*

- When giving a time, make sure that you specify the time zone. For example: *You can reach me by phone from 9 a.m. to 5 p.m. Eastern Standard Time.*

- Remember that the now-common expression 24/7 may be confusing to some customers. Instead, write *You can telephone our customer service department 24 hours a day, 7 days a week.*

- Symbols for weights and measures that we commonly use are not universal. For example, the # for *pound*, the / for *per*, " for *inches*, and ' for *feet*. Write *7 feet, 7 inches* instead of 7' 7".

- Most countries other than the United States use the metric system. For global customers, write numbers metrically or use both U.S. equivalents and metric measures. For example *The length of the raft is 7 feet, 7 inches (230 cm).*

- If you're giving temperatures, give both Fahrenheit and Celsius (centigrade). For example, *The sleeping bag is good for temperatures as low as 32 degrees Fahrenheit (0 degrees Celsius).*

- If you're selling clothes, remember that American sizes aren't universal. Give clothing measurements so that foreign customers can select the right size. For example: *Size medium dresses are 52 inches long (132 cm).*

Be Polite

In the United States we value concise, to-the-point writing. But many cultures consider our style of writing to be abrupt or downright rude. When writing to people in other countries, take extra care to include a friendly greeting in your first paragraph. End your e-mail with a closing paragraph or sentence that emphasizes the polite tone. For more information on tone, see **Chapter 4—Write with a Polite, Positive, and Personal Tone.**

What greeting should you use in your e-mail to foreign customers? Copy the style of greeting in your customer's e-mail. When in doubt, use a more formal greeting: *Dear Mr. LaPella,* rather than the informal *Hi Charlie* or *Hello Charles.*

Avoid Humor

Have you ever watched a British comedy on public television and just didn't get the jokes? Then you'll understand how culturally sensitive humor is. And even without cross-cultural differences, humor is tricky. Maybe you've seen a movie that made you laugh out loud, but your friend, sitting next to you, didn't even smile.

You might think your joke or funny comment makes your e-mail friendly. But your global customer may miss the humor and interpret your words incorrectly. Or your customer may just be confused. Save your humor for jokes that you e-mail to friends! And keep your customer service e-mails polite and friendly but humor free.

Practice 7.4—
Revise the Customer Service Agent's Response to a Global Customer

A non-native English speaker, Ramon Valez, sent this e-mail query to the FireGuarder company. Revise the e-mail response from customer service agent Cynthia. Use the **Checklist: Write for Global Customers** to make sure that your writing will be clear. You may write your changes in the space above each line, or you may use the blank space we've provided on page 135 to rewrite the message entirely. After you finish your revision, compare it to ours on page 150.

Checklist: Write for Global Customers

___ Avoid idioms.

___ Express dates, times, and numbers in terms everyone understands.

___ Be polite.

___ Avoid humor.

Customer E-Mail

> To: customer.service@fireguarder.com
> From: Ramon.valez@homemail.com
> Subject: Problem with Model 380 smoke detector
>
> Dear FireGuarder Company,
>
> It was with great pleasure that I bought a smoke detector from your company.
>
> I have bought one Model 380 smoke detector. But there is problem. It makes noise in the nighttime. But there is no fire. I have put on a new battery, but it makes noise anyway. How can I fix?
>
> I thank you for your kindness,
>
> Ramon Valez

Agent Response

To: Ramon.valez@homemail.com
From: cynthia@fireguarder.com
Subject: Re: Problem with Model 380 smoke detector

Hi Mr. Valez,

This is in response to your e-mail concerning the FireGuarder Model 380 smoke detector. Without seeing the smoke detector, it's hard to figure out what may be wrong. But your best bet is to clean the unit. Vacuum it to remove dust, dirt, and insects (debug it!) that can accumulate in the back of the detector. If you cannot remove the unit's plug before you clean it, shut off the circuit breaker that provides electricity to the smoke detector and place a screwdriver under the lip of the plug and twist. This will move the plug off the pins of the detector.

If you have any further questions, you can contact us 24/7 by e-mail.

Sincerely,

Cynthia
FireGuarder

Practice 7.4—
Revise the Agent's Response to a Global Customer

Practice 7.5—
Write an E-Mail to a Global Customer

Answer this e-mail from a customer in Jakarta, Indonesia. Use the **Checklist: Write for Global Customers** to guide your writing. Write your answer to this customer in the space we've provided on page 137. Show your writing to a colleague or your supervisor for feedback.

Checklist: Write for Global Customers

___ Avoid idioms.

___ Express dates, times, and numbers in terms everyone understands.

___ Be polite.

___ Avoid humor.

Customer E-Mail

> To: customerservice@intertrader.com
> From: Juan@GBS.mex
> Subject: Re: Question on conference
>
> Dear International Trader:
>
> I am very much interested in coming to your interesting and useful conference on Starting an Exporting Business, on 12-14 August 2005. I have many questions. Tell me how much it is to come? How to register? Where to find River Town, Iowa? Is airport for there? Where is good hotel? Is hot weather?
>
> Also, tell me what is "business casual"?
>
> I thank you in advance for your kind help. I hope these are not too many questions for your answer.
>
> With sincere best wishes,
>
> Juan

Practice 7.5—
Your Reply to a Global Customer

If you've studied a foreign language, you've probably found rules about gender confusing. For example, in French and Spanish, every noun has a gender; it's either masculine or feminine. You may have wondered what makes *chocolate* masculine and *apple* feminine.

English presents different gender problems, ones that can puzzle both non-native and native speakers. In English, we've traditionally used masculine words such as *manpower, mailman,* and *chairman* to imply or include both sexes. But sometimes we've developed masculine and feminine forms of the same word to show gender: *stewardess* and *steward; actress* and *actor.*

But as our sensitivity to sexism has increased, we've worked to make our language gender neutral. The business world makes up the "test market" for the glossary of gender-neutral terms. *Human resources* has replaced *manpower, mail carrier* has replaced *mailman,* and *chair* or *chairperson* has replaced *chairman.* We now commonly use *flight attendant* instead of *steward* or *stewardess,* and *salesperson* or *sales rep* to replace *salesman* or *saleswoman.*

Try It

Can you think of gender-neutral words to replace these gender-specific words? Add your gender-neutral replacement to the chart below.

Gender-Specific Word	Gender-Neutral Replacement
chairman	
councilman	
foreman	
housewife	
layman	
mailman	
man-made	
mankind	
manpower	
middleman	
saleslady	
spokesman	
stewardess	
waitress	
workman	

Did you have trouble thinking of a gender-neutral substitute for any of the words on the list? This list has good substitutes for gender-specific words.

Gender-Specific Word	Gender-Neutral Replacement
chairman	chairperson, chair
councilman	council member
foreman	supervisor
housewife	homemaker
layman	layperson
mailman	mail carrier
man-made	artificial
mankind	human
manpower	human resources
middleman	intermediary, go-between
saleslady	salesperson, sales rep
spokesman	spokesperson
stewardess	flight attendant
waitress	server
workman	worker

Avoid Gender-Biased Pronouns

One of the most obvious gender biases in English is our use of personal pronouns. We use gender-nonspecific plural pronouns. For example: *They asked for a refund.* But the singular pronouns we use are gender-specific: the masculine *he, him, his*; or the feminine *she, her, hers*. In English, we've historically used masculine pronouns to imply either gender. For example: *If a customer wants a refund, he should ask for it in writing.*

Four Ways to Eliminate Gender Bias

Try to avoid gender bias in customer service writing. We've rewritten a sentence four ways to show different approaches to eliminating gender bias.

Original sentence:
Each applicant will have his loan documents reviewed by the committee.

1. **Revise using both masculine and feminine pronouns:**
    Each applicant will have his or her loan documents reviewed by the committee.

    (A warning: many writers find this approach produces awkward writing, especially if there are several pronoun references in the e-mail.)

2. **Revise using plural pronouns:**
    Applicants will have their loan documents reviewed by the committee.

3. **Revise by eliminating pronoun reference:**
    The committee will review each applicant's documents.

4. **Revise by using second person pronouns *you* or *your*:**
    The committee will review your loan documents.

Practice 7.6—
Revise a Sentence to Make It Gender Neutral

Try using the four techniques to revise a sentence to make it gender neutral. For answers to **Practice 7.6**, see page 151.

Original sentence:
To get a discount coupon, he must include a current mailing address.

1.   Revise using both masculine and feminine pronouns:

_____

2.   Revise using plural pronouns:

_____

3.   Revise by eliminating pronoun reference:

_____

4.   Revise by using the second person *(you, your):*

_____

Practice 7.7—
Use the Gender-Neutral Checklist to Revise an E-Mail

Use the **Checklist: Five Techniques for Making Your Writing Gender Neutral** to revise this e-mail. Gender-biased pronouns and words are highlighted in **bold**. Write your revisions in the line above the original. For answers to **Practice 7.7**, see page 152.

Checklist: Five Techniques for Making Your Writing Gender Neutral

1.   Use masculine and feminine pronouns *he* or *she, his* or *her*.
2.   Use plural pronouns *they* or *their*.
3.   Eliminate pronoun reference.
4.   Rewrite in the second person using *you* or *your*.
5.   Substitute gender-neutral word for gender-biased word.

Agent E-Mail

To: RandolphK@homemail.com
From   Lisa@youtholympics.org
Subject: Re: Question about Youth Olympics Application

Thanks for your inquiry about your child's participation in the Youth

Olympics. Both boys and girls between the ages of 8 and 12 can

participate in the Olympics.

Your child can check **his** application status by going to the Youth Olympics

home page at www.youtholympics.com. **He** should then enter **his**

password. Once **his** password is confirmed, **he** will then be prompted to

enter the appropriate information in the online application form. When

(continues)

the application is complete, **he** will receive a welcome e-mail from **his** event **chairman**.

We welcome your child's interest in the Youth Olympics. Regardless of the outcome, we know **he** will benefit from the good **sportsmanship** of the competitors.

Thanks --

Lisa
Youth Olympics Information Center

Answers to Practice 7.1—Find Substitutes for Idiomatic Expressions

Did you have trouble thinking of a replacement for some of these expressions? If so, keep this list of useful substitutes nearby.

Idiomatic Expression	Literal Expression
24/7	24 hours a day, seven days a week
a snap	easy
a win-win	where everyone benefits
about time	finally
across the board	includes everything or everyone
ahead of time	early, before
all at once	at the same time
all day long	throughout the day
as a rule	usually, normally
as far as	as for
as soon as	as quickly as
as usual	as always
as well as	in addition to
at a loss	unable: *We were at a loss to explain the issue.* —or— sell something and lose money: *We sold the old computers at a loss.*
at fault	to blame
at last	finally
bar none	without exception
before you know it	quickly
bend over backwards	do everything possible
best bet	best option
bottom line	total, the end result
brand new	newly introduced
bread and butter	principal product (service, business)
brush up	refresh our knowledge of
by the way	incidentally
caught off guard	unprepared for
chairperson	head of the committee, department, organization
change hands	change ownership
change one's mind	reverse a decision

Idiomatic Expression	Literal Expression
close out	sell all
cut back	use fewer, use less
cut corners	economize
cut rate	discount
double-check	check again, confirm
down the road	in the future
dud	failure
fair play	action that is fair
fallen through the cracks	misplaced, forgotten
feel free	please
figure out	find an answer; determine
fill the bill	be just what is needed
first come first served	as long as the supply lasts
flying off the shelf	selling very quickly
from scratch	from the beginning
gain ground	go forward, make progress
get a break	get an opportunity
get in touch with	contact
get off the ground	begin
give the go ahead	approve
give the green light	approve
go through with	proceed
hands-on experience	practical experience
headhunter	job recruiter
hitting the stores	available in the stores
hot deal	special offer
in black and white	in writing
in charge of	responsible for
in lieu of	instead of
in short supply	scarce
in stock	in our current inventory
in the ball park	in the range
in the long run	in the final result
in the works	being planned, in preparation
it goes without saying	it is understood

Idiomatic Expression	Literal Expression
keep track of	keep a record of, stay informed
layaway plan	purchase an item by making partial payment initially, then making monthly payments until it is paid for
let things slide	fail to follow up
level playing field	equalize
more than meets the eye	more than is obvious
on hand	readily available
on the go	busy
on the road	traveling
paperwork	documents
printed matter	printed documents such as brochures, instructions, legal documents, sales contracts
rain check	voucher to be redeemed for an item not currently available
relish the thought	look forward to
rest assured	have our assurance
right up our alley	something we do well
run out	insufficient supply
run short	insufficient supply
sell like hotcakes	sell very fast
short supply	scarce
snap up	to grab quickly
spell out	explain in detail
spread ourselves too thin	try to do too much
stack up	compare favorably to
taken aback	stunned
tall order	difficult assignment
test the waters	try it out
think outside the box	think creatively
to the letter	exactly
touch base	contact
up and running	functioning
weed out	discard
wrap up	finish

Here's one way to revise the e-mail to the customer Naveed. The replacement for the idiomatic expression is written above the idiom.

To: naveed@worldmail.com
From: CustomerService@Camerashops.com
Subject: Re: Where to buy Photopro 680 digital in Washington, D.C.

Thank you for your e-mail about the difficulty of finding a Photopro 680

digital camera in the Washington, D.C., area. We are sorry that you have

not been able to locate this camera in a store in your area. We were
unprepared for
caught off guard by the demand for this camera. They are
selling very quickly   *scarce*
flying off the shelves so that they are in **short supply**.
You have our assurance
Rest assured that we are working hard to see that stores will have them
in their current inventory   as quickly
in stock just **as soon as** we can. The Walmart in your area should have
readily available   *newly introduced*
them **on hand** shortly. You might also be interested in our **brand-new**
available in the stores
Photopro780 camera that will be **hitting the stores** soon. I think that
compares favorably to
you'll find that this new camera **stacks up well against** higher-priced

cameras.

Sincerely,

Jack
Customer Service, Camera Shops

This e-mail contains eight idiomatic expressions. Did you find all of them, or did you miss some because they are so commonly used? In our revised version, the idiomatic expressions are in bold. The replacement is written above.

To:　　　　　Marvelle@worldmail.com
From:　　　　Rita@Tranco.com
Subject:　　　Re: Tranco coffee maker problem

Thanks for contacting us about your problem with your Tranco coffee

Instructions

maker. **Printed matter** explaining how to use the coffee maker should

have been included. I'm attaching the instructions to this e-mail. Using the

easy　　　　　　　　*explain in detail*

coffee maker is **a snap**. The instructions **spell out** the procedure for

brewing coffee. If you follow the instructions for brewing coffee

exactly　　　　　　　　　　　　　*functioning*

to the letter, the coffee maker will be **up and running before**

quickly　　　*It is understood*

you know it. **It goes without saying** that we are very sorry that you

normally

were inconvenienced. **As a rule**, instructions are put inside every box.

Sincerely,

Rita
Tranco Coffee

Answers to Practice 7.4—
Revise the Customer Service Agent's Response to a Global Customer

Here's how we revised the customer service agent's e-mail. The notes in the margins explain the revisions.

To: Ramon.valez@homemail.com
From: cynthia@fireguarder.com
Subject: Re: Problem with Model 380 smoke detector

More formal greeting — Dear Mr. Valez,

Friendly opening — Thanks for writing to us. We are sorry that you are having trouble with the FireGuarder Model 380 smoke detector.

Replaced idiom *figure out* with *determine*

Replaced idiom *best bet*; used *smoke detector* instead of *unit*

Deleted humor *debug it!*

Used *smoke detector* instead of *unit*

Without seeing the smoke detector it's hard to determine what may be wrong. But your problem can often be fixed by cleaning the smoke detector. Vacuum it to remove dust, dirt and insects that can accumulate in the back of the smoke detector. Before you clean it, try to remove the smoke detector's plug. If you can't remove it, shut off the circuit breaker that provides electricity to the smoke detector. Then place the screwdriver under the rim of the plug and twist. This will move the plug off the pins of the smoke detector.

Broke one long sentence into three short sentences; replaced *lip* with *rim*.

Explained *24/7* — If you have any further questions, you can e-mail us seven days a week, 24 hours a day.

Sincerely,

Cynthia
FireGuarder

Answers to Practice 7.6—Revise a Sentence to Make It Gender Neutral

Original sentence:

To get a discount coupon, he must include a current mailing address.

1. Revise using both masculine and feminine pronouns:

   To get a discount coupon, he or she must include a current mailing address.

2. Revise using plural pronouns:

   To get a discount coupon, they must include a current mailing address.

3. Revise by eliminating pronoun reference:

   To get a discount coupon, include a current mailing address.

4. Revise by using the second person pronoun *you*:

   To get a discount coupon, you must include a current mailing address.

Here's how we revised the e-mail to Lisa. Our changes are in **bold** type with a number to indicate which of the **Five Techniques** we used.

Checklist: Five Techniques for Making Your Writing Gender Neutral

1. Use masculine and feminine pronouns *he* or *she, his* or *her.*

2. Use plural pronouns *they* or *their.*

3. Eliminate pronoun reference.

4. Rewrite in the second person using *you* or *your.*

5. Substitute gender-neutral word for gender-biased word.

Revised E-Mail:

To: RandolphK@homemail.com
From: Lisa@youtholympics.org
Subject: Re: Question about Youth Olympics Application

Thanks for your inquiry about your child's participation in the Youth Olympics. Both boys and girls between the ages of 8 and 12 can participate in the Olympics.

Children (2) can check the status of **their** (2) application by going to the Youth Olympics home page at www.youtholympics.com. **Each child** (3) should enter **his or her** (1) password. Once **the** (3) password is confirmed, **the applicant** (3) will then be prompted to enter the appropriate information in the online application form. When the application is complete, the **applicant** (3) will receive a welcome e-mail from **the** (3) event **chairperson** (5).

We welcome your child's interest in the Youth Olympics. Regardless of the outcome, we know **your child** (4) will benefit from the **good conduct** (5) of the competitors.

Thanks --

Lisa
Youth Olympics Information Center

Chapter 8
Put It All Together: Apply What You've Learned about Writing Customer Service E-Mail

In this chapter, you'll practice

Applying what you've learned about writing strong sentences, using an appropriate tone, punctuating and spelling correctly, and writing for global customers

Writing and revising complete e-mail messages to customers

Now it's your turn! This chapter contains seven writing **Practices** that will let you apply all you've learned. For each **Practice**, we've provided the customer's e-mail. In some **Practices**, you'll be revising e-mail responses. For other **Practices**, you'll be writing your own well-written, correct e-mail response. As usual, look at the end of this chapter for sample answers. And refer to the topic and **Practices** in earlier *Workbook* chapters for help as you write.

Good luck!

Practice 8.1—
Correct the Spelling, Punctuation, and Word Usage Errors in This E-Mail

Read the customer's e-mail to the retailer Big Store, then read the agent's response. Correct spelling errors, add or correct punctuation, and substitute the correct word for incorrectly used sound-alike and look-alike words in the agent's response. We've left room for you to make your revisions. Compare your revisions with our version on page 173.

Refer to the following chapters in this *Workbook* while you complete this **Practice**.

Chapter 5—Select the Correct Word and Spell It Right

You learned

- why spelling matters
- how to become a better speller
- how to distinguish between confusing sound-alike and look-alike words

Chapter 6—Punctuate Correctly

You learned punctuation rules for the five most common punctuation marks in customer service e-mail messages:

- period
- comma
- apostrophe
- semicolon
- colon

Customer E-Mail

To: customerservice@BigStore.com
From: ccameron@welr.com
Subject: Returning a videotape

Dear Big Store --

I recently purchased tai chi videotape online. I made my decision to buy the tape based on the reviews on your site. But when I received the tape, I was disappointed. It did not live up to its rave reviews. I'd like to return it. Can I do that?

Thanks,

Carla Cameron

Agent Response

To: ccameron@welr.com
From: customerservice@BigStore.com
Subject: Re: Returning a videotape

Dear Carl Cameron,

Greetings from BigStore.com

I am sorry to here that you we're not satisfied with your VHS tape. I am sorry to advice you that we cannot except these items for return after they have been opened. We are sorry that you did not agree with our reviewers. Before you by a tape make sure it is the one you want.

You can find a copy of our return policy at: http://www.BigStore.com/returns. As this policy specifies you cannot return a tape once you brake the seal on the tape box. We wood have been happy to take the tape back if it were unopened.

However you may want to consider selling this item in our BigStore Marketplace at www.BigStore.com/marketplace. To sell an item access it's detail page on hour Web site than click on the button marked "Sell this item." The next page will outline the steps involved in this process. For further information. Please visit the link below

http://www.BigStore.com/selling

We are truely sorry we could not accomodate your request. Thank you for shoping at BigStore.com we hope to sea you again soon.

Sincerly,
BigStore.com Customer Service

Practice 8.2—Improve the Sentences in This E-Mail

Read the customer's e-mail to Web-Wonderful, a company that provides Web site maintenance and management services. Then improve the sentences in the customer service agent's response.

You can write your edits and revisions to the customer service agent's response in the space provided in the e-mail; however, you may want to rewrite the agent's response entirely. Compare your revisions to **Practice 8.2** with our version on page 175.

As you work on this **Practice**, refer to **Chapter 3—Write Clear, Strong Sentences.**

In **Chapter 3** you learned

- how to write in the active voice
- how to put modifiers in the right place
- how to write full sentences, not run-ons or fragments
- how to choose strong verbs to give your writing power

Customer E-Mail

To: info@Web-Wonderful.com
From: Fred.Marinette@tial.com
Subject: Web-Wonderful Contact Form

Dear Web-Wonderful --

I am interested in learning more about the Web site maintenance and management services your company offers. I am the new webmaster for my company and we are considering outsourcing the day-to-day operation of our site.

Thanks for the information --

Fred Marinette

Agent Response

> To: Fred.Marinette@tial.com
> From: sdeltine@Web-Wonderful.com (Steve Deltine)
> Subject: Re: Web-Wonderful Contact Form
>
> Fred Marinette,
>
> Thank you for your interest. Web-Wonderful specializes in fast, efficient, professional Web site maintenance and management. Our clients count on us to handle all the nearly routine, day-to-day tasks properly necessary to maintain and manage their Web presence. Content maintenance, site performance monitoring, site traffic analysis, promotion.
>
> Three major benefits of using Web-Wonderful verses other methods are quick turnaround, accuracy, and cost savings, we often perform site maintenance in half the time it takes others to perform the same tasks. We offer our clients the ability to enter and monitor the status of maintenance requests via the Web-Wonderful User Panel. It is possible for you to take a tour of the Web-Wonderful User Panel by visiting http://www.Web-Wonderful.com/userpanel.
>
> Pricing is contingent upon your needs. Five hours of work is around $1,000 per month. It is possible for work to be done by us on an as-needed basis.
>
> I would welcome the opportunity to discuss your needs in more detail. Please let me know the best way to set up a phone conversation.
>
> Sincerely,
>
> Steve Deltine
> *Web-Wonderful, Inc.*

Your Rewrite to Improve Sentences

Clear, Correct, Concise E-Mail

Practice 8.3—Improve the Customer Service Agent's Tone in This E-Mail

In this **Practice**, you will be reading an ongoing e-mail exchange between a customer and a PhoneCo customer service agent. PhoneCo is a long-distance telephone service provider.

Read the customer's e-mail. (The customer has sent e-mail messages to PhoneCo before.) Then, revise the customer service agent's response to improve the tone.

Use the *Checklist: Write with a Polite, Positive, and Personal Tone* on page 160 to guide you as you improve the PhoneCo agent's tone.

We've left room in the agent's response for you to make revisions, but you may want to rewrite the agent's response entirely. Compare your revisions with our version on page 176.

As you work on this **Practice**, refer to **Chapter 4—Write with a Polite, Positive, and Personal Tone.** You learned

- how words affect tone

- how personalizing your e-mail makes customers feel valued

- how plain, simple language contributes to a polite, positive, and personal tone

Customer E-Mail

From: melinda@workwell.net
To: metrocustcare@phoneco.com
Subject: WT21220107_1212120346 030 359 5875 121

Dear PhoneCo Customer Service:

I have another question. In looking over my phone bill, I see that you are charging a long-distance fee. As I understood my service, the long-distance billing would begin on Nov. 20 when I switched to you as my long-distance provider. On my bill it says my billing cycle began on Nov. 13, but I was connected on Nov. 20, 2004. Thank you.

Melinda Aristotle

Agent Response

From: metrocustcare@phoneco.com
To: melinda@workwell.net
Subject: Re: WT21220107_1212120346 030 359 5875 121

Please include the following line in all replies.
Tracking number: WT21220107_1212012346

Attn: Melinda Aristotle

Account number: 030 359 5875 121

You contacted us on Jan. 3 regarding the incorrect address on your bill.

This is a different request that should have been sent as a new and

separate request. Page 5 of the bill will give you what the charge is for.

Any charges on your account will be broken down on the bill. Any new

requests will need to be sent as a new and separate e-mail. Our long

distance billing cycle begins on the 13th of the month for everyone. Your

account will be credited for the 7 days before you became our long

distance customer. It says so on page 5 of your bill.

Rhonda
PhoneCo Customer Care

Checklist: Write with a Polite, Positive, and Personal Tone

___ Use the customer's name in the greeting.

___ Set the tone with a personalized opening.

___ Use personal pronouns *(I, we, our, you, your)*.

___ Avoid angry words or phrases.

___ Avoid inflated words or phrases.

___ Avoid insider's language.

___ Reinforce the tone with a personal closing.

Practice 8.4—
Answer a Customer's Angry E-Mail with a Polite, Positive, and Personal Tone

The customer, Barry Hess, a building contractor, is angry because his Web sites have been submitted to a construction site listing service—TwobyFour.com—without his permission. The customer's tone is confrontational and rude. In the response, the customer service agent uses a similar angry tone.

Revise the response from agent Patrick Eason so that the tone is polite, positive, and personal.

We've left room for you to make revisions, or you may rewrite the agent's message entirely. Compare your revisions with our version on page 177.

As you work on this **Practice**, refer to **Chapter 4—Write with a Polite, Positive, and Personal Tone.** You learned

- how words affect tone

- how personalizing your e-mail makes customers feel valued

- how plain, simple language contributes to a polite, positive, and professional tone

Customer E-Mail

From: hess@virtualconstruction.com
To: peason@TwobyFour.com
Subject: site listings

Dear Patrick Eason,

What's the matter with you??!! Help me understand why you have submitted two of my Web sites, www.constructionmaterials.com and www.deckbuilder.com, to your construction Web sites listing service. I did not request this. I refuse to pay the $175 fee. Please explain.

Thank you,

Barry Hess
President
The Virtual Construction Corp.

Agent Response

From: peason@TwobyFour.com
To: hess@virtualconstruction.com
Subject: Re: site listings

Dear Mr. Hess --

Perhaps this was not a request that you personally made, but it was

entered into my Category 1900096 as a submission to be reviewed

and approved.

We are all very new with TwobyFour.com and still learning necessary

procedures to process and serve all to the best of our abilities. I will try to

make the necessary arrangements to remove you, if you so desire. If the

$175 fee is a problem for you, we will consider a refund.

Sincerely,

Patrick Eason
Customer Service Agent, TwobyFour.com

Your Revision to Improve Tone

Practice 8.5—
Answer a Global Customer's E-Mail Using Idiom-Free, Gender-Neutral Language

Read the customer's e-mail to USAVacationFun.com, a company that rents vacation properties all across America. Then revise the customer service agent's e-mail response to eliminate words or phrases that might be confusing to a global customer or that may show a gender bias. In the agent's response, we've left room for you to make your revisions. Compare your revisions to our version on page 178.

As you work on this **Practice**, refer to **Chapter 7—Write for Global Customers.** You learned

- how to identify idioms that are confusing to non-native English speakers and how to replace them with literal expressions

- how to write customer service e-mail that is sensitive to cultural differences

- how to write gender-neutral e-mail

Customer E-Mail

To: USAVacationFun.com
From: ElenaMast@mail.it
Subject: Please TO SEND information about booking

Please to send me information about booking the beach cottage "West Wind" in Monterey, California in week 5 August 2005.
We stay one week. What is the fee? Thank you.

Elena Mastrontonio

Agent Response

To: ElenaMast@mail.it
From: USAVacationfun.com
Subject: Re: Please TO SEND information about booking

Hey, Elena!

Thanks for stopping by USAVacationfun.com. The information you supplied has been sent on to the property owner or agent for the advertised vacation property. He'll get in touch soon.

Please be patient as it may take 24 to 48 hours for him to respond (more if he's on the road). If you don't get a response within a reasonable period of time -- please click back to http://www.USAvacationfun.com/Monterey1331 and complete the online request form again, or make contact via phone. Call from 9-5, Mon-Fri.

I think you'll die for Monterey. The beach is great and there are lots of happening clubs, restaurants, etc. There's even a vegan take-out called Sprouts and Such for you to try. And the weather's great, mostly. You know what they say about California weather: if you don't like it, just wait 10 minutes!

If you need to contact someone regarding the USAVacationfun.com Web site, please send e-mail to webmaster@USAVacationfun.com.

Happy Travels!!!

Cynthia
Customer Service

Practice 8.6—
Answer a Customer's E-Mail about a Product

Now you get to answer a customer's e-mail and apply all the writing skills you've learned. Mitchell Aimel has written to Drink Soy, Inc. to say that he is unhappy with the soymilk maker the company manufactures.

We've provided a **Fact Sheet** for you to use to answer Mitchell Aimel's e-mail. You may use some or all of this information in writing your response. You should also invent any information you need to answer the customer's question completely.

Remember what you've learned and practiced throughout the *Workbook*:

• Write clear strong sentences.

• Use a positive, professional tone.

• Select the correct word and spell it right.

• Punctuate correctly.

• Use language global customers will understand.

When you've finished, compare your e-mail with our version on page 179.

Customer E-Mail

From: Mitchell [mAimel@zzz.com]
To: service@drinksoyinc.com
Subject: Watery soy milk

Dear Drink Soy, Inc.:

I purchased your Drink Soy soymilk maker recently and the first couple of batches of soymilk that we made were fine. After we used up the soybeans you sent to us we have tried two other kinds of soybeans and it looks like the Drink Soy machine is not grinding the soybeans up properly.

We get watery soymilk. My wife has thrown out our last batch and gone back to buying soy milk from the store. We bought your Drink Soy machine so we would not have to use store-bought soymilk. We have tried doing a double batch or soaking the soybeans longer but we still are getting watery, clear soymilk.

I called daily this week but no one has returned my call. My phone number is 555-622-5411. Here is the information about my order: Invoice #9222 on 2/9/05 for $225. I need help either fixing this problem or getting an address for returning the machine for refund.

Thank you.
Mitchell Aimel

Fact Sheet for Answering Mitchell Aimel's E-Mail for Drink Soy, Inc.

1. This customer called Drink Soy, Inc. on 9-27-04 at 11:32 a.m. No record of any other calls.

2. A clogged filter is causing the problems the customer describes.

3. Any kind of soybean will work in this machine.

4. Find tips on cleaning the filter at www.drinksoyinc.com/cleantips.html.

5. Suggest Drink Soy's Greenfilter Detergent to clean the filter. In a large container, dissolve two tablespoons of Greenfilter Detergent in a half gallon of water. Submerge the filter. Soak overnight.

6. Greenfilter Detergent product information:
   - An 8-oz. bag costs $7.
   - Shipping and handling is $3 for each order.
   - An 8-oz. bag has enough detergent for five uses.
   - Greenfilter Detergent is non-toxic and biodegradable.
   - Purchase Greenfilter Detergent online at www.drinksoyinc.com/onlineorder or by calling 1-800-DRINKSOY.

Your Response to Mitchell Aimel's E-Mail

Practice 8.7—
Answer a Customer's E-Mail about a Service

Now you'll answer a customer's question about a service. In this **Practice**, you'll write an e-mail to answer Lisa LaPorta's inquiry about GreenGrassNow.com's lawn mowing services. She wants to know whether she can afford the service. We've provided a **Fact Sheet** for you to use to respond to her e-mail. You may use some or all of this information in writing your response. You should also invent any information you need to answer the customer's question completely.

Remember what you've learned and practiced throughout the *Workbook*:

- Write clear, strong sentences.

- Use a positive, professional tone.

- Select the correct word and spell it right.

- Punctuate correctly.

- Use language global customers will understand.

When you've finished, compare your e-mail with our version on page 180.

Customer E-Mail

To:	sales@GreenGrassNow.com
From:	Lisalaporta@webfriend.com
Subject:	Need information about lawn mowing services

Dear GreenGrassNow.com --

I am interested in your lawn mowing services, but I want to know whether I can afford your service. I can probably afford about $75 per month. Do you have a limited service option for people like me who are on a budget? I have a small yard with several trees and three flower gardens and a large vegetable garden.

Thanks --

Lisa LaPorta

Fact Sheet for Answering Lisa LaPorta's E-Mail to GreenGrassNow.com

1. Three pricing plans:

   - Full summer of lawn mowing (April through October) for $600.
   - Monthly fee (weekly mowing) of $100.
   - With the "Mow As You Go" pricing plan you pay for each mowing. The cost is $35 per mowing for quarter-acre lawns and $50 per mowing for half-acre lawns.

2. We offer the following services in addition to lawn mowing:

   - Renovate overgrown gardens
   - Install decks and fences
   - Design and install garden lighting
   - Install automatic irrigation systems
   - Build water gardens and install fountains

3. If you call us for a free estimate, we will give you a free lawn analysis complete with a soil test from your lawn, a $30 value.

4. Customer can reply to this e-mail or call 1-800-977-7870.

Your Response to Lisa LaPorta's E-Mail

Answers to Practice 8.1—
Correct the Spelling, Punctuation, and Word Usage Errors in This E-Mail

We've written the correct word above the error (in bold type). Punctuation changes are in brackets [ ].

Customer Service Agent Response

From: customerservice@BigStore.com
To: ccameron@welr.com
Subject: Re: Returning a videotape

Carla

Dear **Carl** Cameron,

Greetings from BigStore.com[**.**]

hear   *were*

I am sorry to **here** that you **we're** not satisfied with your VHS tape. I am

advise   *accept*

sorry to **advice** you that we cannot **except** these items for return after

they have been opened. We are sorry that you did not agree with our

buy

reviewers. Before you **by** a tape[**,**] make sure it is the one you want.

You can find a copy of our return policy at http://www.bigStore.com/returns.

break

As this policy specifies[**,**] you cannot return a tape once you **brake**

would

the seal on the tape box. We **wood** have been happy to take the tape

back if it were unopened.

However[**,**] you may want to consider selling this item on our BigStore

its   *our*

Marketplace. To sell an item[**,**] access **it's** detail page on **hour** Web site

then

than click on the button marked "Sell this item." The next page will outline

please

the steps involved in this process. For further information[**,**] **P**lease visit

the link below[**.**]

http://www.bigStore.com/selling

truly   *accommodate*

We are **truly** sorry we could not **accomodate** your request. Thank you

shopping   *We*   *see*

for **shoping** at BigStore.com[**.**] **w**e hope to **sea** you again soon.

Sincerely

Sincerly,

BigStore.com Customer Service

Answers to Practice 8.2—Improve the Sentences in This E-Mail

Here's how we improved the sentences in this e-mail. Your revisions might be slightly different from the ones we show here. Our revisions appear in **bold** type.

To: Fred.Marinette@tial.com
From: sdeltine@Web-Wonderful.com (Steve Deltine)
Subject: Re: Web-Wonderful Contact Form

Fred Marinette,

Thank you for your interest. Web-Wonderful specializes in fast, efficient, professional Web site maintenance and management. Our clients count on us to handle **nearly** all the routine, day-to-day tasks necessary to **properly** maintain and manage their Web presence. **Web-Wonderful offers the following services:** content maintenance, site performance monitoring, site traffic analysis, **and** promotion.

Three major benefits of using Web-Wonderful are quick turnaround, accuracy, and cost savings. **We** often perform site maintenance in half the time it takes others to perform the same tasks. We offer our clients the ability to enter and monitor the status of maintenance requests via the Web-Wonderful User Panel. **You may tour** the Web-Wonderful User Panel by visiting http://www.Web-Wonderful.com/userpanel.

Pricing is contingent upon your needs. Five hours of work **costs** around $1,000 per month. **We can work for you** on an as-needed basis.

I welcome the opportunity to discuss your needs in more detail. Please let me know the best way to set up a phone conversation.

Sincerely,

Steve Deltine
Web-Wonderful, Inc.

Here's how we revised the e-mail to Melinda Aristotle using a polite, positive, and personal tone. Your revisions may be different; compare the changes you made with the changes here. You may want to show your revised e-mail to a friend or colleague to get some feedback on what you've written. Does your reader think your response has the proper tone?

From: metrocustcare@phoneco.com
To: melinda@workwell.net
Subject: Re: WT21220107_1212120346 030 359 5875 121

Please include the following line in all replies. Tracking number:
WT21220107_1212012346

Attn: Melinda Aristotle
Account number: 030 359 5875 121

Dear Melinda:

Thank you for your question about the start date of your billing cycle. You asked why your billing cycle began on November 13, 2004, when your service was connected on November 20, 2004. Please let me explain: PhoneCo's long-distance billing cycle begins on the 13th of the month for everyone. We will credit your account $13.45 for the seven days before you became our long-distance customer. Page 5 of your bill explains this account credit process. The tracking number for your question about your billing cycle is WT21220107_1212012346. Please include this tracking number in all e-mail you send us about your billing cycle.

You also e-mailed us on January 3 regarding the incorrect address on your bill. We have corrected your address, as you requested. The tracking number for your question about your address is WT2133037_19898123. Please include this tracking number in any other e-mail you send us about the address on your bill.

We are glad to have you as a new PhoneCo customer. Please contact us by e-mail or by telephone at 800-999-2323 if you have questions about your service.

Rhonda
PhoneCo Customer Care

This revised e-mail response to Barry Hess has a polite, positive, and personal tone. Your revision may be different; compare the changes you made with this revised e-mail. You may want to show your revised e-mail to a friend or colleague to get some feedback on what you've written. Does your reader agree that the tone of your revised response is helpful and apologetic instead of rude?

To: hess@virtualconstruction.com
From: peason@TwobyFour.com
Subject: Re: site listings

Dear Mr. Hess,

I am sorry your Web sites -- www.constructionmaterials.com and www.deckbuilder.com -- were submitted to TwobyFour.com without your permission or approval. I am checking into how this mistake happened, and I will e-mail you within a week with an explanation. Please accept my apology for your inconvenience and for sending you an invoice for $175. Of course we have canceled the charge. We have mailed you a statement showing that your account has no balance.

To try to make up for our error, we would like to offer you a FREE listing with TwobyFour.com. Would you be interested in listing both sites with us for the next three months? The fee for listing two sites for three months is $350, but we will waive the fee for you. Please respond to this e-mail if you are interested in this offer.

Again, I apologize for the confusion. I hope you'll consider a free trial of TwobyFour.com. I think you'll be pleased with our site-listing service if you give us a try.

Sincerely,

Patrick Eason
Customer Service, TwobyFour.com

Here's how we revised the e-mail to Elena Mastrononio. Your revisions may be different because there is more than one way to revise this e-mail to make it gender neutral and clear to a global customer.

Our revisions appear in **bold** type.

To: Elena Mastrontonio
From: USAVacationfun.com
Subject: Re: Please TO SEND information about booking

Hello, Elena Mastrontonio:

Thanks for **visiting** USAVacationfun.com. The information you supplied has been sent on to the property owner or agent for the advertised vacation property. **The property owner will call or e-mail you soon.**

Please be patient, as it may take 24 to 48 hours for the owner to respond. **(It may take more time if the owner is traveling.)** If you don't get a response within a reasonable period of time, **please visit our site again -- http://www.USAVacationfun.com/Monterey1331 to complete the online request form one more time. Or, you can call us during our normal business hours: Monday through Friday from 9 a.m. until 5 p.m. Eastern Standard Time.**

I think you'll **enjoy** Monterey, **California**. The beach is beautiful and there are lots of **lively** clubs **and** restaurants. **You might even like to try a new vegan restaurant** called Sprouts and Such. And the **weather in Monterey is normally very good**. **But** California weather **has a reputation for changing quickly!**

If you need to contact someone regarding the USAVacationfun.com Web site, please send e-mail to webmaster@USAVacationfun.com.

Enjoy your vacation!

Cynthia
Customer Service

Answer to Practice 8.6—Answer a Customer's E-Mail about a Product

Here's how we answered Mitchell Aimel's e-mail about his problems with his soymilk maker. Your e-mail may be different from the one presented here. You may want to show your e-mail to a friend or a colleague to get some feedback on what you've written.

To: Mitchell [mAimel@zzz.com]
From: service@drinksoyinc.com
Subject: Re: Watery soymilk

Dear Mitchell Aimel,

Thank you for contacting Drink Soy, Inc. about your soymilk maker. We're sorry you're not satisfied with the soymilk you've been making recently, but we're certain you can make delicious soymilk with the Drink Soy machine. All you need to do to solve the problems you described is clean the filter thoroughly and regularly. A clogged filter is causing the grinding problems you're having with the machine.

Our Web site offers tips on cleaning the Drink Soy's filter at www.drinksoyinc.com/cleantips.html. We suggest that you use Greenfilter Detergent to clean the Drink Soy's filter. You can purchase Greenfilter Detergent online at www.drinksoyinc.com/onlineorder or by calling 800-DRINKSOY.

Greenfilter Detergent is non-toxic and biodegradable. To clean the machine's filter, you simply dissolve two tablespoons of Greenfilter Detergent in a half gallon of water. Submerge the filter in the detergent/water solution and soak the filter overnight.

Once you clean the filter, your Drink Soy machine will be making excellent soymilk again. Please call or e-mail me if you have any other questions about your Drink Soy machine or the other products we sell for health-conscious people.

Sincerely,

Erin Pomeroy
Drink Soy Customer Service Agent

Here's how we answered Lisa LaPorta's inquiry about lawn mowing services offered by GreenGrassNow.com. Your e-mail may be different from the one presented here. You may want to show your e-mail to a friend or a colleague to get some feedback on what you've written.

To: Lisalaporta@webfriend.com
From: Steve.Clement@GreenGrassNow.com
Subject: GreenGrassNow mowing services are within your budget

Dear Lisa,

Thank you for contacting GreenGrassNow.com about our lawn mowing services. I am certain we can provide excellent service within your budget. In fact, we are glad to give you a free estimate. Just reply to this e-mail or call us at 800-555-7870 to request the estimate. And, with your free estimate, GreenGrassNow will give you a free lawn analysis complete with a soil test, a $30 value absolutely free.

We offer three pricing plans for our mowing services. From the budget you mentioned in your e-mail, I think our "Mow As You Go" pricing plan might be best for you. With "Mow As You Go" you pay for each mowing you schedule. The cost is $35 per mowing for quarter-acre lawns. Our second pricing plan is a full summer of lawn mowing (April through October) for $600. The third pricing plan is a monthly fee of $100. For a flat monthly fee of $100 we will mow your lawn weekly.

You also mentioned that you have several trees, flower gardens, and a vegetable garden. GreenGrassNow can help you keep all your gardens looking great. We install garden lighting, automatic irrigation systems, and fountains. We'd be glad to tell you more about these services. At the Portfolio page at our Web site, you can see examples of gardens we've improved.

Thanks again for your interest in our services. Please call us at 800-977-7870 or e-mail us right away to schedule your free estimate.

Sincerely,

Steve Clement, Customer Care Agent
GreenGrassNow.com

Chapter 9
Resources

This chapter includes three resource lists:

Online Resources on E-Mail Writing
Online Resources on Grammar and Usage
General Writing Resources in Print

Online Resources on E-Mail Writing

A Beginner's Guide to Effective Email
Kaitlin Duck Sherwood's guide, advice, books, resource lists, examples, and exercises make this one of the best Web sites on this topic.
http://www.webfoot.com/advice/email.top.html

Emailreplies.com
A comprehensive guide to e-mail etiquette and policies.
http://www.emailreplies.com

E-Mail: Top 10 Tips for Writing it Effectively
Guidance from University of Wisconsin (Dennis G. Jerz and Jessica Bauer). Detailed, easy to read and follow, good links to other sources of information.
http://www.uwec.edu/jerzdg/orr/handouts/TW/e-mail.htm

Google's E-Mail Help and Tutorial
Everything from tips for managing overload to security and effective writing.
http://directory.google.com/Top/Computers/Internet/Email/FAQs,_Help,_and_Tutorials/

20 Rules for Writing Effective Business E-Mails
Paul Soltoff's advice on how to avoid fluff and spin by providing benefits and facts.
http://www.businesscomputing.com/emarketing/article.php/221882

Online Resources on Grammar and Usage

Guide to Grammar and Writing
A comprehensive resource on writing covering topics from grammar to report planning. Test your knowledge with a variety of quizzes on all aspects of English, including grammar and punctuation. Quizzes provide instant answers. E-mail your grammar questions to "Ask Grammar." Hosted by Charles Darling, Professor of English at Capital Community-Technical College, Hartford, Connecticut.
http://www.ccc.commnet.edu/grammar/

Indispensable Writing Resources
A linked directory of resources for writers, including an index for technical and business writing, online writing labs, and grammar and usage Web sites.
http://www.quintcareers.com/writing/writweb.html

Online Technical Writing Textbook
Technical writing textbook with chapters on technical reports, proposals, abstracts. Includes sample documents.
http://www.io.com/~hcexres/tcm1603/acchtml/acctoc.html

The Blue Book of Grammar and Punctuation
Concise, easy-to-understand explanation of grammar, punctuation, and usage rules. Also practice exercises and tests.
http://www.grammarbook.com/

Commonly Confused Words
An extensive alphabetical list of commonly confused words.
http://www.pnl.gov/ag/usage/confuse.html

ESL Idiom Page from Dave's ESL Café
Large list of idioms with explanations and sample sentences. Useful to people for whom English is a second language and native English speakers who want to be aware of idioms when writing for non-native English speakers.
http://eslcafe.com/idioms/

Top Ten Least Wanted Phrases in Business Writing
Ten annoying phrases to keep out of your e-mails.
http://www.westwords.com/GUFFEY/topten.html

Language Sites on the Internet
Long and lively list of resources in a range of categories: etymology, grammar and usage, even puns.
http://www.verbivore.com/rllink.htm

General Writing Resources in Print

Alred, Gerald J., et al. *The Business Writer's Handbook,* 7th ed. St. Martin's Press, 2003.

The American Heritage English As a Second Language Dictionary, Houghton Mifflin, 1998.

The AP Stylebook, Basic Books, 2004

Azar, Betty Schrampfer. *Understanding and Using English Grammar,* 3rd ed. Longman Publishing Group, 2001.

Booher, Dianna. *E-Writing: 21st Century Tools for Effective Communication,* Pocket Books, 2001.

Camp, Beth. *Effective Workplace Writing,* McGraw-Hill, 1997.

The Chicago Manual of Style, 15th ed. University of Chicago Press, 2003.

EEI Press, *E-What? A Guide to the Quirks of New Media Style and Usage,* 2000.

Harris, Muriel. *Prentice Hall Reference Guide to Grammar and Usage,* 5th ed. Prentice Hall, 2002.

Lanham, Richard A. *Revising Prose,* 4th ed. Longman Publishing Group, 1999.

Ober, Scot. *Contemporary Business Communication,* 5th ed. Houghton Mifflin, 2002.

O'Conner, Patricia T. *Woe Is I: The Grammarphobe's Guide to Better English in Plain English,* 2nd ed. Riverhead Books, 2004.

Rubens, Philip, gen. ed. *Science and Technical Writing: A Manual of Style,* 2nd ed. Routledge, 2000.

Sabin, William A. *The Gregg Reference Manual*, 10th ed. McGraw-Hill, 2004.

Smith, Lisa A. *Business E-Mail: How to Make It Professional and Effective,* Writing and Editing at Work, 2002.

Strunk and White. *The Elements of Style,* 4th ed. Longman Publishing Group, 2000.

Truss, Lynne. *Eats, Shoots & Leaves: The Zero Tolerance Approach to Punctuation,* Gotham Books, 2004.

Notes

Notes

Order Form

Clear, Correct, Concise E-Mail: *A Writing Workbook for Customer Service Agents*

Fax orders:	Fax this form to 301–718–8021
Telephone orders:	Call E-WRITE toll free at 1–877–481–1869 or 301–989–9583
E-mail orders:	orders@WritingWorkbook.com
Postal orders:	E-WRITE, 407 Scott Drive, Silver Spring, MD 20904-1065, USA.
Internet orders:	www.WritingWorkbook.com

ITEM	PRICE (USD)	QUANTITY	TOTAL
Clear, Correct, Concise E-Mail **(Print)**	$34.95		
E-Mail Writing Skills Competency Exam **(Print)** (includes Exam, Administrator's Guide, Certificate of Completion, Certificate of Competency)	$50.00		
Clear, Correct, Concise E-Mail + Competency Exam **(Print)**	$79.00 (save $14.95)		
Order and Download PDF at: www. writingworkbook.com			
Clear, Correct, Concise E-Mail	$29.95		
E-Mail Writing Skills Competency Exam (includes Exam, Administrator's Guide, Certificate of Completion, Certificate of Competency)	$45.00		
Clear, Correct, Concise E-Mail + Competency Exam	$69.00		

Order online at www.WritingWorkbook.com

	SUBTOTAL from above	
Contact us for discounts on more than 10 print copies and to license PDF of *Clear, Correct, Concise E-Mail*, and E-Mail Writing Skills Competency Exam		
U.S. Shipping and Handling: Select Option 1 *or* Option 2		
Option 1: Shipping and handling by USPS Media Mail (book rate); delivery in 7–15 days	**FREE** *(FREE shipping is NOT available for International orders.)*	
Option 2: Rush: Shipping and handling (delivery 1-3 days) $5.00 per item		
INTERNATIONAL Shipping and Handling: USPS Global Priority Mail	30% of total purchase	
Sales tax: Add 5% for products shipped to Maryland addresses		
	TOTAL	

TO:

Name

Company

Address

City   State   Zip

Country

Telephone

Fax

E-mail

PAYMENT

☐ Check (in US$) payable to E-WRITE, LLC

☐ Money order (in US$)

Credit Card

☐ Visa   ☐ Mastercard   ☐ American Express

Card number

Name on card

Expiration date

Questions? Call E-WRITE toll free at 1–877–481–1869; Fax 301–718–8021; e-mail *orders@WritingWorkbook.com*

Please send FREE information on E-WRITE's other products and services

☐ Training: customized writing courses for your organization   ☐ Writing services: web and e-newsletters

☐ Speaking/Presentations   ☐ Articles for reprint in your publication